The North End Football Team

The noble game of football is all the rage, you'll ow
And lately in that kind of sport, Proud Preston she has shown;
That in her town she does possess the men, I'm proud to say,
Who now can play and beat some of the crack teams of the day.

Chorus
Shout hurrah for the North End Football team,
To try and win the English Cup they mean,
We will dance and sing with joy when they win the final tie;
Shout hurrah for the North End Football team.

We've Dewhurst on the Left Wing, and Smalley by his side,
With the ball between them, down the field they very quickly glide.
There's Belger in the centre, the favourite of all,
The lad that puts the shakers on the keepers of the goal.
Chorus. – Shout hurrah, &c.

With Drummond on the Right Wing and the famous Gordon too,
In the whole United Kingdom their equals are but few,
With Russell, Wilson, Robinson, I'm sure it is a treat;
When Russell's on the leather, with his India rubber feet.
Chorus. – Shout hurrah, &c.

There's Duckworth at the back, his play is good none can deny,
And many is the time that he's protected Billy Joy;
Led on by Ross the Captain, and all admit and say,
That Ross is now the finest back in England to-day.
Chorus. – Shout hurrah, &c.

So let us wish them all success and coupled with it too,
Their umpire Mr Sudell, their friend so staunch and true,
Long life and luck attend their lot wherever they may be;
And may the team take good advice from one that is Jim Lee.
Chorus. – Shout hurrah, &c.

By Mr G. B. Browne, the Author and Composer of the above song, sung nightly by him with
great success in the music halls of Preston, circa 1884.

1.
ORIGINS
*

2.
HOME
*

3.
THE BIRTH
OF FOOTBALL
*

4.
ESTABLISHED
*

5.
CONSTRUCTION
*

6.
DEBARRED
*

7.
CHANGE
*

8.
ON THE ROAD
*

9.
WINNING
*

10.
FOUNDERS
*

11.
INVINCIBLE
*

PRESTON NORTH END – THE RISE OF THE
INVINCIBLES

WRITTEN BY

MICHAEL BARRETT

ILLUSTRATED BY

DAVID SQUE

Invincible Books

Preston

For Mum, and Uncle Martin – a North Ender.
MJB

First published in 2016 by Invincible Books Limited

Website: www.invinciblebooks.co.uk

Email: michael@invinciblebooks.co.uk

Photo credits and thanks to The National Football Museum, Guardian News & Media Ltd, and Preston Digital Archive.

This book is inspired by real events. Some dialogue has been created.

ISBN: 978-0-9956023-0-4
Published by Invincible Books Ltd in 2016
Edited by Stan Carey   www.stancarey.com
Printed by GraphyCEMS   www.graficascems.com

FOREWORD

'Ahh – Preston North End.'

How many times have we heard that?

Wherever we are in the world, it seems someone has heard of our hometown club. Among fans of British football clubs it is well known of the achievements of North End's famous double-winning side – the team that won the first ever Football League and the FA Cup in the same season, without experiencing a single defeat.

As a local lad, apprentice and former West Stand season ticket holder, I was brought up on the legends of the Deepdale greats, and I was delighted to be asked to write this foreword. The pages of this book bring to life the early history of PNE in a way that is reminiscent of the comic books of old, and to see such players as Geordie Drummond, Fred Dewhurst and Nick Ross take to the field is fantastic. The earliest known recordings of North End matches are from the early 1900s, so for the Invincibles, this is probably as close as we can get! Looking through this book it is fascinating to see the Victorian fans surround the pitch and to see how football fever took hold of Preston. Looking at their reactions, it is certainly fair to say that some things never change!

What has changed are the boots and the kits (sometimes not for the better), and as for team formations – can you see any team taking to the field with six forwards these days?! It is also remarkable to witness the steady transformation of Deepdale. That old farm on the hill is now one of the oldest continually used football grounds in the world – could they ever have imagined that?

They say football is a sport of opinions, and that is true. But it is also true to say that the achievements of William Sudell and his team have yet to be equalled – and no matter how rival fans may argue, no club has a history like North End. The importance of the part they played in the formation and progress of the game cannot be overestimated. The story of the famous Invincibles has been a source of pride and interest for the people of Preston for generations, and now that story is brought vividly to life in the pages of this book.

I for one have thoroughly enjoyed reading it, and I hope you will too.

Mark Lawrenson

INTRODUCTION

A funny thing happened to me while researching this book. I became a fan. Not a newly converted fan of Preston North End, no – having grown up only minutes from their home at Deepdale Stadium, I'd always followed the fortunes of the Lilywhites. But rather, I became a fan of the Victorian version of PNE.

Trawling through the newspaper archive at the Harris Museum and reading match reports from the 1880s, I found myself questioning any account that went against the North End men. If Davie Russell and Jack Graham had been 'outclassed' in the middle, or Nick Ross easily pushed off the ball (something I can't believe ever happened), or if Jack Belger had been anything less than prolific, then I refused to believe it. I didn't question anything biased in their favour, of course.

I realised that in reading the articles, I was experiencing the past in real time – as a North Ender would have done all those years ago – and I was probably reacting in the exact same way!

The football action in the present pages is taken from those very newspaper accounts, and retold through the vibrant illustrations of artist David Sque. For many years David worked on the famous *Roy of the Rovers* comic, and it is fitting that he has now illustrated the *Invincibles*, for their journey truly was Roy of the Rovers stuff!

Through 11 chapters we chart that journey from North End's birth in the 1860s to their unbeaten season of 1888–89. Along the way, we take in the Industrial Revolution, the American Civil War, the Lancashire Cotton Famine and two Preston Guilds – offering a social history alongside that of a football club. And as Prestonians know, this isn't just any football club! North End's pioneering team were the sporting superstars of their day. Even aside from their glorious double-winning season, the club's role as a founding member of the Football League, and in the fight for professionalism, assures them an esteemed place in the annals of football history.

The story of the Invincibles is truly a remarkable tale, and one I feel privileged to have had the chance to study and document in this way. Now that it's done, I can only thank you in advance for reading it, and sincerely hope you feel I've done justice to an amazing time in the history of Preston North End FC.

Michael Barrett, July 2016

ORIGINS

Hurry – the parade's started!

ALTHOUGH THE COTTON MILLS WERE AT THE HEART OF THE INDUSTRIAL REVOLUTION - THANKS IN PART TO RICHARD ARKWRIGHT'S BRILLIANCE - THEIR VAST PROFITS DIDN'T REACH THE WORKERS' POCKETS, AND AN OVERCROWDED TOWN SUFFERED FROM POOR HOUSING AND DISEASE.

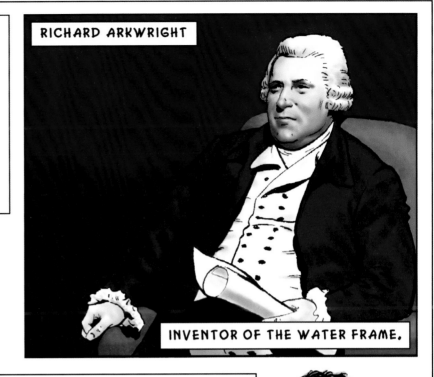

RICHARD ARKWRIGHT

INVENTOR OF THE WATER FRAME.

HARD TIMES

CHARLES DICKENS

INDEED, THE MISERY INSPIRED CHARLES DICKENS, WHO VISITED PRESTON IN 1854 AND USED IT AS THE BASIS FOR COKESTOWN IN HIS NOVEL *HARD TIMES.*

"It was a town of red brick or of brick that would have been red if the smoke and ashes had allowed it: but, as matters stood, it was a town of unnatural red and black...It was a town of machinery and tall chimneys, out of which interminable serpents of smoke trailed themselves for ever and ever, and never got uncoiled...factories looming heavy in the black wet night - their tall chimneys rising up into the air, competing Towers of Babel.

7 YEARS LATER IN 1861, AND CONFLICT IN AMERICA...

OH NO!

THE TIMES

CIVIL WAR IN AMERICA

UNION STATES FIGHT THE CONFEDERATES

... TRIGGERED DISASTER IN LANCASHIRE.

ABRAHAM LINCOLN SOUGHT TO WEAKEN THE CONFEDERATE ARMY.

BLOCKADE ALL THE SOUTHERN PORTS!

YES, MR PRESIDENT.

THE BLOCKADE CUT OFF ALL SHIPMENTS OF RAW COTTON TO ENGLAND, RESULTING IN THE LANCASHIRE COTTON FAMINE OF *1861-1865.*

THIS MILL IS CLOSED

SORRY FOLKS, NO COTTON... NO WORK.

BUT US JOBS?!

WITH NO COTTON, MANY MILLS SIMPLY SHUT DOWN, AND PRESTON WAS HARDEST HIT. BY *1862,* THOUSANDS WERE UNEMPLOYED AND STARVING.

WHAT'LL WE DO NOW...?

EMERGENCY RELIEF COMMITTEES WERE SET UP TO HELP THE POOR.

AND FOOD AND CLOTHING GIVEN TO THOSE IN NEED.

IN THE MIDST OF THESE TRAGIC CIRCUMSTANCES ARRIVED THE PRESTON GUILD OF *1862*. FEELINGS ABOUT THE GUILD WERE MIXED. WITH THOUSANDS LEFT DESTITUTE BY THE COTTON FAMINE, MANY COULDN'T UNDERSTAND HOW HUGE AMOUNTS COULD BE SPENT ON CELEBRATIONS. YET PRESTON'S OFFICIALDOM WEREN'T PREPARED TO LET ANCIENT TRADITIONS PASS BY — AND THE GUILD WENT AHEAD.

HURRY — THE PARADE'S STARTED!

GUILD 62

PRESTON'S UNIQUE *20* YEARS CELEBRATION UNITED ALL SECTIONS OF THE COMMUNITY.

GOD SAVE THE QUEEN

OVER *600,000* ATTEND THE FESTIVITIES FROM FAR AND WIDE! THE OFFICIAL LINE SPOKE OF A WELCOME BOOST FOR THE TOWNSFOLK AND DECLARED THE GUILD A BIG SUCCESS.

THE MARSH, PRESTON,

IN THE ENCLOSED GROUND.

EXTRAORDINARY ATTRACTION

MONDAY, SEPTEMBER 1st, 1862.

IN THE "GUILD" WEEK.

THE WORLD-RENOWNED

BLONDIN

THE HERO

WILL GIVE

OF NIAGARA

HIS

WONDERFUL

PERFORMANCE

OF

THE HIGH ROPE!

SUROUNDED BY FIREWORKS

A MAJOR HIGHLIGHT WAS A SENSATIONAL TIGHT ROPE WALK OVER PRESTON MARSH, BY WORLD FAMOUS ACROBAT, JEAN-FRANCOIS GRAVELET, ALSO KNOWN AS *THE GREAT BLONDIN!*

IT'S IN THESE CONFLICTED TIMES OF CELEBRATION AND DISTRESS, THAT WE TRACE THE ORIGINS OF OUR BELOVED PRESTON NORTH END. FOR DURING THESE YEARS A GROUP OF MEN GATHERED EACH WEEK ON THE SAME LAND OF PRESTON MARSH.

FROM THIS GROUP, STEPPED FORTH THE BASIS OF THE VERY FIRST PRESTON NORTH END CLUB. THEY GATHERED EACH WEEK TO PLAY...

AS THE COTTON FAMINE CONTINUED, TENSIONS ROSE IN LANCASHIRE. WHILST MANY SYMPATHISED WITH ABRAHAM LINCOLN'S QUEST, OTHERS REBELLED AT THE LOSS OF THEIR LIVELIHOODS AND RIOTS BROKE OUT.

THE GOVERNMENT REACTED.

WE CAN'T RISK AN UPRISING!

RELIEF IS RUNNING DRY!

WE MUST CREATE JOBS!

PUBLIC WORKS (MANUFACTURING DISTRICTS) ACT, 1863-1864

PRESTON CORPORATION MADE QUICK USE OF THE PUBLIC WORKS FUND.

TOWN PLANNING

ALLOW ME TO PRESENT! NEW ROADS... A NEW TOWN HALL... AND...

THE PLANS BROUGHT MUCH NEEDED EMPLOYMENT AND INCLUDED THE LANDSCAPING OF THE ANCIENT MOOR IN THE NORTH OF PRESTON – MOOR PARK.

A FEATURE OF THE NEWLY LANDSCAPED PARK WAS A MUNICIPAL CRICKET PITCH. UP AND RUNNING BY *1866*, IT QUICKLY PROVED AN ATTRACTIVE LURE FOR THE TOWN'S CLUBS.

AROUND THIS TIME, A SPLIT OCCURRED WITHIN BOW LANE CRICKET CLUB AND A BREAKAWAY GROUP CALLED 'NELSON' MOVED AWAY FROM THE MARSH TO THE NEW MOOR PARK. WHAT HAPPENED NEXT IS UNCLEAR – EITHER ANOTHER SPLIT OCCURRED IN THE NEWLY FORMED NELSON, OR THEY CHANGED THEIR NAME BECAUSE A TEAM OF THE SAME ALREADY EXISTED.

BOW LANE C.C.

NELSON C.C.

WHAT IS CLEAR IS THAT BY THE TIME MOOR PARK OFFICIALLY OPENED IN OCTOBER OF 1867, TWO TEAMS HAD BEEN COMPETING THROUGHOUT THE SUMMER, ONE NAMED NELSON CRICKET CLUB, AND THE OTHER – THE NORTH END CRICKET CLUB.

NORTH END C.C.

CHOOSING THEIR NAME FROM THE AREA OF PRESTON IN WHICH THEY WERE FORMED, THE CLUB'S TITLE MORPHED BETWEEN **THE NORTH END** – TO **NORTH END PRESTON** – TO **PRESTON NORTH END** – AND THEN BACK TO **THE NORTH END**!

BUT IT MATTERS LITTLE, EITHER WAY, THE ORGANISATION WE KNOW TODAY AS **PRESTON NORTH END** HAD FINALLY ARRIVED – ALBEIT AS A CRICKET CLUB!

NORTH END WASTED LITTLE TIME. GEORGE HOWARTH BECAME THEIR FIRST PRESIDENT AND W.W. HULME CLUB SECRETARY. MEMBERS WERE OPENLY WELCOMED FROM BOTH WORKING CLASS AND WELL-TO-DO BACKGROUNDS; A REFRESHING, ALL-FOR-ONE ETHOS PREVAILED.

NO JOINING FEE LADS – JUST TUPPENCE A WEEK!

ALTHOUGH STRUGGLING FINANCIALLY, NORTH END PROGRESSED QUICKLY, ATTRACTING SUPPORT FROM ALL SECTIONS OF THE COMMUNITY.

ONE NEW RECRUIT, A WELL-CONNECTED 16 YEAR OLD, WAS TO HAVE A MAJOR IMPACT ON THE CLUB'S FUTURE. HIS NAME...

WELCOME TO THE CLUB, BILLY!

...WILLIAM SUDELL.

SPLENDID PLAY!

C'MON TH' NORTH END!

MATCHES WERE VIEWED AS RESPECTABLE SOCIAL OUTINGS (ALTHOUGH MUCH DRINKING AND GAMBLING TOOK PLACE!) AND THE CLUB FORMED GOOD RELATIONS WITH THE LOCAL PRESS.

ON THE 20TH JULY, 1867, **THE PRESTON GUARDIAN** REPORTED:

The North End team of; W. Marchbank, J. Marchbank, Banks, Sumner, Green, Woods, Hulme, Goddard, Berry, Wilson, and Almond, defeated Fulwood Garrison, in heavy rain by 15 on the first innings. During the game, players and friends enjoyed liberal refreshments supplied by the Garrison!

ATHLETIC FESTIVALS.

IN THE *1870*S A NEW CONFIDENCE ARRIVED IN PRESTON. THE COTTON FAMINE WAS OVER AND SOCIAL CONDITIONS WERE IMPROVING. CRICKET WAS AS POPULAR AS EVER AND PRESTON WAS EXPERIENCING SOMETHING OF A SPORTING BOOM.

SWIMMING AT SAUL STREET BATHS.

BOAT RACES ON THE RIBBLE.

ICE SKATING ON MOOR PARK.

CAPTURED IN THIS BOOM, AMIDST RISING AMBITION, NORTH END REALISED THAT IN ORDER TO SURVIVE, THEY NEEDED THE SPACE TO GROW. THEY NEEDED A PLACE TO PLANT DREAMS AND LAY FOUNDATIONS, A PLACE TO BECOME THE CLUB THEY WANTED TO BE.

THEY NEEDED A HOME.

HOME

Socker?
Aye, the dribblin' game, son.

BY THE EARLY 1870S, NORTH END WERE WELL ESTABLISHED, BOTH ON THE FIELD AND OFF IT. THEY ENJOYED END-OF-SEASON SUPPERS AT THE PORT ADMIRAL HOTEL ON LANCASTER ROAD, AND ANNUAL BALLS IN THE ASSEMBLY ROOMS OF THE CORN EXCHANGE.

THE CLUB BEGAN TO SURROUND ITSELF WITH INFLUENTIAL PEOPLE, AND ITS ANNUAL BALL IN DECEMBER 1874 CONTAINED SOME RATHER GRAND ATTENDEES.

THE NIGHT WAS A FINANCIAL AND SOCIAL SUCCESS.

ONE NEWSPAPER REPORTED: ...A THRONG OF 300... KEPT THE DANCING UP WITH UNABATED SPIRIT AND DECORUM UNTIL 3AM.

NEW CLUB SECRETARY WILLIAM NAYLOR AND NEW CHAIRMAN WILLIAM SUDELL WERE DELIGHTED. BOLSTERING THE CLUB'S ACCOUNTS GAVE FRESH IMPETUS TO A LONG-HELD GOAL, AND THE FOLLOWING MONTH SAW NORTH END TAKE WHAT PROVED TO BE A CHARACTERISTIC LEAP OF FAITH – THEY'D FOUND A HOME!

JUST EAST OF MOOR PARK LAY DEEPDALE FARM. ALTHOUGH PHYSICALLY NOT A GREAT DISTANCE, IT WAS IN EVERY OTHER SENSE A MASSIVE MOVE.

OLD HEY FIELD

THE FIVE-ACRE HOLDING OF OLD HEY FIELD, SLOPING SLIGHTLY DOWNHILL FROM SOUTH TO NORTH, WAS LEASED ON THE 21ST JANUARY 1875, ACCORDING TO PROMINENT SPORTS JOURNALIST JIMMY CATTON. A FEW DAYS LATER WILLIAM NAYLOR PLACED AN ADVERT.

PRESTON NORTH END CRICKET CLUB

Announce our opening game of the season, on Sat, 25th March, 1875, on our new 'Private Ground' at Deepdale.

WITH A GROUND TO PAY FOR, NORTH END NOW HAD TO GENERATE AN INCOME, NOT MERELY SURVIVE. TO ATTRACT CROWDS THEY EXHIBITED VARIOUS SPORTS, INCLUDING LACROSSE, ROUNDERS AND THAT OBVIOUS CROWD-PULLER...

... CLOWN CRICKET!

ALL FAILED.

UNDETERRED, THE CLUB STROVE ON, AS REPORTER JIMMY CATTON LATER RECALLED:

I remember well what an enthusiastic little band those men were. They improved their pitch, and built a small pavilion, while in 1876 they inaugurated an athletics festival.

THE NORTH END C.C. ATHLETICS FESTIVAL AT DEEPDALE

AY UP?

CLUB MEMBERS USED THEIR CONNECTIONS TO ARRANGE AN ATHLETICS FESTIVAL IN ASSOCIATION WITH THE **PRESTON GYMNASTICS AND ATHLETICS CLUB.**

AWARE OF THE TOWN'S GROWING PASSION FOR SPORT – ENCOURAGED THROUGH IMPROVED WAGES, AND THE *1874* WORK ACT – THE FESTIVAL WAS A CALCULATED RISK, AND DEEPDALE WAS TRANSFORMED.

A STAND WAS ASSEMBLED, REFRESHMENT BARS SET UP AND A RUNNING TRACK FENCED OFF. NUMEROUS CONTESTS TOOK PLACE, AND THERE WAS EVEN MUSIC FROM THE *11*TH LANCASHIRE ROYAL VOLUNTEERS BAND! IT WAS A RESOUNDING TRIUMPH, WITH OVER *5,000* PEOPLE ATTENDING!

EVENTS INCLUDED A BICYCLE RACE.

NORTH ENDER HARRY CARTMELL CAME 2ND IN THE 120 YARDS.

WHILE THE **NORTH END PULLBACKS** LITERALLY FELL TO DEFEAT IN THE TUG-O-WAR!

BUOYED BY THE FESTIVAL, SUDELL NOW SOUGHT A NEW SPORT. PRESTON'S SUMMERS AREN'T KNOWN FOR BEING LONG, AND DEEPDALE NEEDED TO PROVIDE AN INCOME DURING ITS WINTER MONTHS.

SEPTEMBER 1876, AT THE DEEPDALE BRIDGE HOTEL.

I PROPOSE THE FORMATION OF A RUGBY FOOTBALL CLUB.

30 MEMBERS SIGNED UP.

TWO WEEKS LATER.

J. SINGLETON, CAPTAIN. J. WILSON, SUB-CAPTAIN.

...CLUB COLOURS, ORANGE AND BLACK.

ORANGE AND BLACK?!

MANY CRICKET CLUBS HAD FORMED RUGBY SIDES, AND NORTH END'S FIRST GAME WAS AGAINST OLD CRICKETING RIVALS PRESTON OLYMPIC.

IN STORMY CONDITIONS THEY LOST BY 3 TRIES TO 2 TOUCHDOWNS.

ANOTHER LOSS FOLLOWED – THIS TIME AWAY TO PENWORTHAM ROVERS.

THINK I PREFER CRICKET!

BUT YOU CAN'T KEEP GOOD MEN DOWN, AND INCREDIBLY, THEY WENT THE REST OF THE SEASON UNDEFEATED!

THE NORTH END RUGBY TEAM, 1877

BACK, L TO R: T WADESON, T PARKINSON, F. DODGSON, JOHN SINGLETON, TED TOWERS, HARRY CARTMELL, JOHN SUMNER. MIDDLE: JACK PARKINSON, JOE WILSON, BILLY SHARPLES, JACK HAROLD, JOHN WADESON, FRED MAYOR. FRONT: JACK HULME, BILL CHARNLEY, BOBBY GREEN, WILLIAM SUDELL.

THEN, IN 1878...

WE ARE TO PLAY EAGLEY... AT ASSOCIATION RULES.

ASSOCIATION RULES?

THA' MEANS SOCCER.

SOCKER?

AYE, THE DRIBBLIN' GAME, SON.

ALL IN FAVOUR, SAY AYE!

THE BIRTH OF FOOTBALL

Is that a goal?!
What's a goal?

BALL GAMES ARE NOTHING NEW.

IN CHINA, THE GAME OF CUJU ('KICK-BALL') WAS PLAYED AS EARLY AS 2000 BC. USING SKILL AND TECHNIQUE, A STITCHED LEATHER BALL IS KICKED THROUGH A TARGET SUSPENDED 9 FEET HIGH ON BAMBOO POLES.

THE ANCIENT ROMAN EMPIRE PLAYED HARPASTUM – A GAME THEY ADAPTED FROM THE GREEK SPORT HARPASTON. POPULAR WITH ITS CITIZENS, IT WAS ALSO EMPLOYED AS A TRAINING REGIME BY THE ROMAN ARMY, AND IS PERHAPS CLOSER TO RUGBY THAN FOOTBALL.

IN THE 1500s, SPANISH CONQUISTADORS DISCOVERED AZTECS PLAYING THE FEROCIOUS ULLAMALIZTLI ('BALL GAME').

WOW, A RUBBER BALL!

WHAT'S RUBBER?

I DUNNO.

DESCENDING FROM MAYAN CULTURE, ULLAMALIZTLI WAS STEEPED IN SYMBOLISM AND RELIGIOUS MEANING, AND WAS A MAJOR PART OF AZTEC LIFE.

ALL THESE AND OTHER ANCIENT BALL GAMES ARE STILL PRACTISED AROUND THE WORLD TODAY, BUT ARE ANY RELATED TO MODERN FOOTBALL? MOST HISTORIANS THINK NOT, CLAIMING INSTEAD THAT THE ROOTS OF OUR BEAUTIFUL GAME LIE MUCH CLOSER TO HOME – IN THE FIELDS AND VILLAGES OF BYGONE BRITAIN.

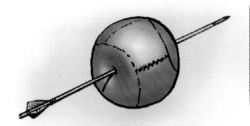

BALL GAMES AND VARIANTS OF FOOTBALL HAVE BEEN PLAYED IN BRITAIN FOR CENTURIES. IN *1365*, EDWARD III FORBADE FOOTBALL FOR '*ITS TENDANCY TO IMPEDE THE CULTIVATION OF ARCHERY*.'

BY THE *1700s*, FOLK FOOTBALL WAS LONG EMBEDDED IN PEASANT CULTURE, AND GAMES OF MASS OR 'MOB' FOOTBALL WERE COMMON, RITUALISTIC EVENTS. OPPOSING VILLAGE OR PARISH TEAMS COUNTED HUNDREDS ON EACH SIDE, AND THE RULES WERE SIMPLE – GET THE BALL TO YOUR TARGET, BY FAIR MEANS OR FOUL!

THE UPPER CLASSES DETESTED THESE GAMES, FEARING THAT THE MAYHEM COULD SPILL OUT INTO FULL-SCALE RIOTS. INDEED, AFTER VISITING ENGLAND IN THE *1840s*, A FRENCHMAN FAMOUSLY REMARKED:

IF ENGLISHMEN CALLED THIS PLAYING, IT WOULD BE IMPOSSIBLE TO SAY WHAT THEY WOULD CALL FIGHTING!

NOT ALL GAMES WERE LARGE, VIOLENT AFFAIRS. SMALLER MATCHES, MORE AKIN TO MODERN STREET-FOOTBALL, WERE PLAYED IN POCKETS ALL OVER BRITAIN. RULES WERE SOPHISTICATED AND LOCALISED, WITH TEAMS OF EQUAL SIZE DRAWN FROM ALL WALKS OF LIFE.

1683: BUTCHERS v. GLOVERS.

1747: LADIES 6-A-SIDE.

YET FOLK FOOTBALL WAS UNDER ATTACK, FROM BOTH THE NERVOUS RULING CLASSES AND THE CHANGING WORLD. MOB GAMES WERE SEEN AS UNDIGNIFIED, AND THE ONSET OF THE INDUSTRIAL REVOLUTION MEANT LESS TIME AND FEWER OPEN SPACES IN WHICH TO PLAY.

FOOTBALL WAS IN DANGER OF DYING OUT. BUT HELP WAS AT HAND, AND IT WAS TO COME, CONVERSELY, FROM THE SONS OF THE RULING CLASSES.

IN THE *1800s*, FOOTBALL WAS A MAJOR PART OF PUBLIC-SCHOOL LIFE, AND EACH SCHOOL HAD ITS OWN UNIQUE (AND QUIRKY) RULES.

IS THAT A GOAL?!

WHAT'S A GOAL?

ETON HAD TWO CODES, THE 'FIELD GAME' AND THE 'WALL GAME'. IN ETON'S WALL GAME, DECADES CAN PASS WITHOUT A GOAL!

RUGBY WAS THE FIRST SCHOOL TO ALLOW CARRYING THE BALL WHEN RUNNING.

WHILE HARROW PLAYED WITH A BALL SHAPED LIKE A GIANT PIE!

IN *1848*, EAGER TO CONTINUE PLAYING FOOTBALL, EX-PUBLIC SCHOOLBOYS GOT TOGETHER AT CAMBRIDGE UNIVERSITY TO DEVISE A UNIFORM SET OF RULES.

I'M SORRY, OLD CHAP, BUT YOUR BALL JUST ISN'T A BALL!

THEY HAD SOME SUCCESS, BUT ULTIMATELY CONFUSION REIGNED, AS MANY 'OLD BOYS' CONTINUED PLAYING TO THEIR OWN ACCUSTOMED RULES.

IT WASN'T UNTIL A CERTAIN MR EBENEZER COBB MORLEY WROTE A LETTER TO THE *BELL'S LIFE* NEWSPAPER IN AUGUST, *1863*, THAT FOOTBALL BEGAN TO MOVE FORWARD.

EBENEZER'S LETTER PROPOSED THAT CLUBS GATHER TO HAMMER OUT A UNIFORM SET OF RULES. AND SO A SERIES OF HEATED MEETINGS TOOK PLACE IN THE FREEMASON'S TAVERN, GREAT QUEEN STREET, LONDON.

KICKING.

SHINNING.

CARRYING.

HACKING.

SHEFFIELD RULES.

PREDICTABLY, A DECISION TO PLEASE EVERYONE COULD NOT BE REACHED. THE BLACKHEATH CLUB, WHO FAVOURED HACKING (KICKING BELOW THE KNEE) AND RUNNING WITH THE BALL IN HAND, LEFT THE TALKS TO HELP DEVELOP THE RUGBY CODE, AND THE 'KICKING' AND 'DRIBBLING' ENTHUSIASTS EMERGED WITH A NEW SET OF RULES!

THE FOOTBALL ASSOCIATION WAS BORN!

AGREED!

FOR THE NEXT THREE YEARS THE FA STRUGGLED. CLUBS AROUND THE COUNTRY OFTEN PLAYED TO THEIR OWN RULES, OR FLITTED BETWEEN THE RUGBY AND ASSOCIATION CODES.

IT WASN'T UNTIL **1866**, WHEN CHARLES ALCOCK JOINED THE FA COMMITTEE, THAT THINGS IMPROVED. HIS EFFORTS HELPED REFINE THE RULES, BRINGING THEM MORE INTO LINE WITH THOSE OF CHARTERHOUSE, WESTMINSTER, AND SHEFFIELD FOOTBALL CLUB - WHO'D BECOME A MAJOR FORCE IN THE NORTH. GRADUAL CHANGES INCLUDED:

TAPE FOR A CROSSBAR -

8 FEET HIGH.

NO HANDLING -

ONLY KEEPERS.

GOAL KICKS AND CORNER KICKS.

LOOK, 'TIS SIMPLE - AN ATTACKER IS OFFSIDE IF HE'S IN FRONT OF THE THIRD-LAST DEFENDER.

THREE-MAN OFFSIDE RULE.

THEN, ON THE *20ᵀʰ JULY, 1871,* CHARLES ALCOCK HAD AN INSPIRED IDEA...

A CHALLENGE CUP SHOULD BE ESTABLISHED... FOR WHICH ALL CLUBS BELONGING TO THE ASSOCIATION SHOULD BE INVITED TO COMPETE!

A TROPHY WAS COMMISSIONED, *18* INCHES TALL AND COSTING *£20.00* — THE **FA CHALLENGE CUP!**

ON THE *16ᵀʰ MARCH, 1872,* AT THE KENNINGTON OVAL IN LONDON, A CROWD OF OVER *2,000* PEOPLE WATCHED WANDERERS BEAT THE ROYAL ENGINEERS, *1-0,* TO BECOME THE FIRST EVER WINNERS OF THE FA CUP.

BUT THE NEWS THAT 'BESSIE', A LARGE BROWN BEAR, HAD ESCAPED IN CRICKLEWOOD WAS OF MORE INTEREST TO READERS OF THE LONDON PAPERS THAT WEEKEND!

OUR BEAUTIFUL GAME WAS UP AND RUNNING – BUT IT STILL HAD A LONG WAY TO GO!

ESTABLISHED

Eh? Tis 'lectric, Luv – the future!

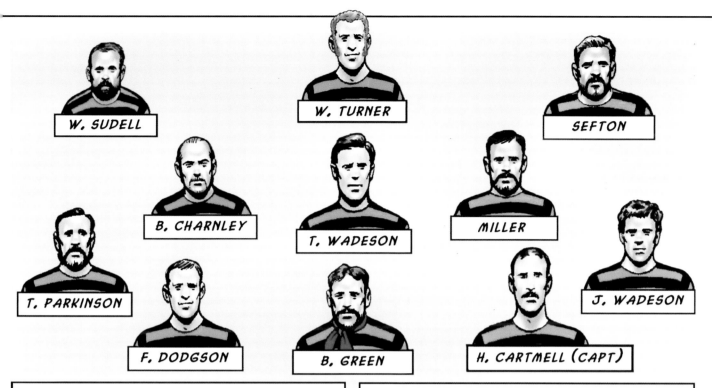

W. SUDELL

W. TURNER

SEFTON

B. CHARNLEY

T. WADESON

MILLER

T. PARKINSON

J. WADESON

F. DODGSON

B. GREEN

H. CARTMELL (CAPT)

NORTH END WERE HEAVY UNDERDOGS.

BUT THEY PUT UP A GOOD SHOW...

THAS THE STUFF!

...AND ONLY LOST...

UGH!

...TO A DEFLECTED GOAL IN THE SECOND HALF.

AFTERWARDS, *THE PRESTON CHRONICLE* REPORTED:

...being played under the Association Rules, it was thought defeat for the North End was a foregone conclusion. A more evenly and hotly contested a a game, however, was never witnessed on this ground before. The play of both sides cannot be too highly praised, and it would be invidious to mention any particular player, as each played with remarkable energy and pluck to gain victory for his side.

BY 'ECK, 'ARK AT THIS! THE VERY NOVEL BUT HIGHLY INTERESTING. MODE OF PLAYING FOOTBALL BY ELECTRIC LIGHT WILL BE INTRODUCED IN PRESTON ON THURSDAY NIGHT NEXT. OOOOOOH!

WHY NOT JUST PLAY DURIN' DAY?

EH? TIS 'LECTRIC, LUV — THE FUTURE!

TIS DAFT, IS WHAT IT IS!

WELL, 'AM GOIN!

AYE? YOU'LL BE ON THAS OWN!

THIS TRIAL WITH ELECTRIC LIGHTING HIGHLIGHTED NORTH END'S PROGRESSIVE SPIRIT AND WILLINGNESS TO TRY NEW VENTURES.

THE EQUIPMENT WAS SUPPLIED BY PARK AND BIBBY OF MANCHESTER...

...AND THE CURIOUS FOLK OF PRESTON TURNED UP IN DROVES TO SEE THE NIGHT SKY ILLUMINATED OVER DEEPDALE!

ANYONE GOT A MATCH?!

TIS DAFT THIS!

THAS WOT MI MISSUS SAID.

BUT UNFORTUNATELY, AN ACCIDENT TO THE APPARATUS LEFT FANS AND PLAYERS IN THE DARK.

SADLY, THE NIGHT WAS DEEMED A FAILURE. WITH ENTRANCE FEES REFUNDED, IT WAS A BLOW TO BOTH THE CLUB'S PRIDE AND ITS STRAINED FINANCES.

STILL, THE GOOD NEWS WAS THAT NORTH END DID WIN THE GAME! AND BY THE END OF THE SEASON THEIR RUGBY TEAM BOASTED AN IMPRESSIVE RECORD: PLAYED 15, WON 10, DRAWN 2, LOST 3 (1 ASSOCIATION RULES).

DESPITE SUCCESS AT RUGBY, NORTH END WERE KEEN FOR ANOTHER BASH AT ASSOCIATION RULES, AND IN NOVEMBER *1879* THEY INVITED HALLIWELL TO DEEPDALE.

AGAIN THEY LOST, *1-0*. BUT SOMETHING HAD TAKEN HOLD, AND JUST *6* MONTHS LATER THE MOST DEFINING MEETING IN THE CLUB'S SHORT HISTORY TOOK PLACE.

MONDAY *10*TH MAY, *1880*, THE DEEPDALE BRIDGE HOTEL.

IT IS PROPOSED BY HARRY CARTMELL AND SECONDED BY TOM CHARNLEY, THAT THE NORTH END CLUB SHOULD JOIN THE LANCASHIRE ASSOCIATION FOOTBALL UNION, AND HENCEFORTH PLAY SOCCER UNDER THEIR RULES.

ALL THOSE IN FAVOUR...

MOTION PASSED!

THE PRESTON NORTH END ASSOCIATION FOOTBALL CLUB, WAS ESTABLISHED!

THE CLUB'S NAME WOULD BE CHANGED TO THE ALL-ENCOMPASSING *PRESTON ATHLETIC SOCIETY & NORTH END CRICKET & FOOTBALL CLUB!*

HAVING PLAYED ONLY *2* GAMES IN *2* YEARS, NORTH END WERE NOW COMMITTED TO ASSOCIATION FOOTBALL. NO ONE PRESENT COULD HAVE IMAGINED THE SIGNIFICANCE OF THAT DECISION.

A NEW ERA HAD BEGUN.

IN JUNE, NORTH END JOINED THE LANCASHIRE FOOTBALL ASSOCIATION (WHICH HAD BEEN FOUNDED IN *1878*) AND GAINED ENTRY INTO THE LFA CUP.

SOME MEMBERS BEGAN TO VIEW SOCCER AS A POSSIBLE ANSWER TO THE CLUB'S FINANCIAL WOES. ALTHOUGH SUCCESSFUL AT RUGBY, THEY'D STRUGGLED TO ATTRACT CROWDS, WITH THE MORE ESTABLISHED PRESTON GRASSHOPPERS ENTICING THE LION'S SHARE OF THE TOWN'S FANS.

THEY'D ALSO NOTED THE SUCCESS OF FELLOW LANCASHIRE TEAMS AMIDST SOCCER'S GROWING POPULARITY IN THE NORTH.

THE LANCS FA CUP.

BLACKBURN ROVERS

DARWEN

BOLTON WANDERERS

BLACKBURN OLYMPIC

INDEED, IN NOVEMBER, A CROWD OF OVER *10,000* WATCHED BLACKBURN ROVERS v. DARWEN!

NORTH END WERE FAR BEHIND THEIR LANCASHIRE RIVALS — THEY HADN'T YET SCORED A GOAL, NEVER MIND WON A GAME! BUT THEY HAD TO START SOMEWHERE, AND THEIR INTENTION TO LEARN FROM THE BEST BROUGHT ADMIRATION FROM *THE PRESTON HERALD*:

The Preston North End Football Club, though young in the Association game, has been able to complete a list of matches which does credit to everyone concerned. Some of the best clubs in the county figure upon their list of fixtures, which ought to be a great stimulus to the game, in a district where the Rugby Union holds undisputed sway.

ON SATURDAY 9ᵀᴴ OCTOBER, 1880, BEFORE A CROWD OF AROUND 800, NORTH END CONCEDED 14 GOALS AT HOME TO DARWEN.

BUT IT WASN'T ALL BAD. THEY NO LONGER WORE ORANGE, FOR A START! AND 5 MINUTES FROM TIME, WITH THE SCORE 0-13, NORTH END'S FORWARDS (ALL SIX OF THEM) MADE A MAGNIFICENT RUSH TOWARDS THE DARWEN END TO SCORE THE CLUB'S FIRST EVER RECORDED GOAL!

BUT WHO GOT THE FINAL TOUCH?

THE *PRESTON HERALD* CLAIMED IT WAS BILL CHARNLEY!

WHILE THE *PRESTON GUARDIAN* CREDITED HARRY CARTMELL!

PROBABILITY RESTS WITH HARRY CARTMELL, AS A FORWARD – BUT CAN WE BE CERTAIN?

THE CLUB'S FIRST WIN IS ALSO TINGED WITH UNCERTAINTY. ON SATURDAY 27ᵀᴴ NOVEMBER, A WEEK AFTER LOSING THEIR OPENING LFA CUP TIE 6-0 AWAY TO TURTON, THEY FACED THE WELL-ESTABLISHED ASTLEY BRIDGE AT DEEPDALE.

TOWARDS THE END OF THE FIRST HALF, COOKSON SCORED HIS SECOND GOAL TO PUT NORTH END 2-0 UP, BUT ASTLEY'S UMPIRE ARGUED IT WAS OFFSIDE. NATURALLY, NORTH END DISAGREED! AS NO REFEREE HAD BEEN APPOINTED, IT WAS AGREED TO CALL THIS A DISPUTED GOAL!

OFFSIDE!

GOAL!

IN THE SECOND HALF ASTLEY BRIDGE EQUALISED AND THE MATCH FINISHED 1-1. BUT PNE CLAIMED VICTORY WITH THEIR DISPUTED GOAL!

THE FOLLOWING WEEK, NO SUCH DOUBT EXISTED. AS COX GREEN OF BOLTON WERE BRUSHED ASIDE 3-0, THANKS TO GOALS FROM AINSWORTH AND NUTTALL (2).
TWO WINS IN A ROW? DISPUTED OR NOT, IT SEEMED NORTH END WERE GETTING TO GRIPS WITH THE DRIBBLING GAME.

THE GAMES CONTINUED, AND ON THE 26TH MARCH 1881, THE MIGHTY BLACKBURN ROVERS ARRIVED AT DEEPDALE.

NORTH END KICKED OFF JUST AFTER 4 PM.

4.15: BATEMAN'S TRICKERY WAS CAUSING PROBLEMS.

BUT AT 4.17...

4.18...

4.20...

AND IT DIDN'T STOP THERE...

FINAL SCORE: 16-0.

THE DRUBBING BY ROVERS WAS HARD TO TAKE, BUT THE MEN FROM DEEPDALE PERSEVERED, AND THE FOLLOWING SEASON, ALTHOUGH DIFFICULT, BROUGHT SOME HIGH POINTS...

LIKE THE *12-3* THRASHING OF STACKSTEADS WORKING MEN, IN ROUND *2* OF THE LFA CUP!

IT'S TWELVE!

TURTON (AGAIN) KNOCKED THEM OUT, WINNING 8-0, IN THE NEXT ROUND. EVEN SO, WHEN BLACKBURN ROVERS RETURNED TO DEEPDALE IN THE GUILD YEAR OF *1882*, THERE WAS A GROWING OPTIMISM AMONG THE DEEPDALE FAITHFUL.

HOWEVER...

FLAMIN' 'ECK! WOT CAN THEE DO?!

STOP PLAYIN' ROVERS, FOR A START!

BETTER THAN LAST TIME, THO'.

NORTH END   2.
BLACKBURN R.   11.

DESPITE LOSING THE FIRST EVER GUILD WEEK FOOTBALL MATCH, NORTH ENDERS AND THEIR FELLOW PRESTONIANS STILL HAD PLENTY TO CHEER, AS THE '82 GUILD WAS VOTED THE BEST EVER!

EVENTS THAT YEAR INCLUDED...

A FANTASTICAL TORCHLIGHT PARADE...

LAYING OF THE FOUNDATION STONE FOR THE HARRIS FREE LIBRARY...

AN IMPROVED TRAM SYSTEM – INCLUDING A NEW ROUTE FROM FISHERGATE TO THE PLEASURE GARDENS OF NEW HALL LANE...

AND SEVERAL BALLOON ASCENTS FROM AVENHAM PARK, BY THE FEARLESS CAPTAIN MORTON!

AFTER TWO SEASONS OF FOOTBALL, THINGS WERE TAKING SHAPE AT DEEPDALE.

JAMES McDADE, THE CLUB'S FIRST SCOTTISH PLAYER, WAS A GUIDING VOICE ON TACTICS, WHILE OUTSIDE LESSONS ARRIVED IN THE LECTURES OF EX-DARWEN PLAYER JAMES GLEDHILL. THE CHARISMATIC GLEDHILL'S FOOTBALL PHILOSOPHY GREATLY IMPRESSED WILLIAM SUDELL, WHO BEGAN TO IMPLEMENT HIS IDEAS AT NORTH END.

PROGRESS WAS QUICK. SOON SUDELL WAS CLAIMING NORTH END WERE THE BEST TEAM IN PRESTON – AND FEW COULD DISAGREE.

STAR PLAYERS AT THE TIME INCLUDED:

BETHEL ROBINSON: INFLUENTIAL PLAYER AND MEMBER.

WILLIAM JOY: FIRST-CHOICE GOALKEEPER.

FRED DEWHURST: TALENTED FORWARD FROM FULWOOD, AND A MASTER AT PRESTON CATHOLIC COLLEGE.

JOHN BELGER: NEW CAPTAIN AND CROWD FAVOURITE. A GENTLE, QUIET MAN OFF THE PITCH, KNOWN AS 'THE GOALKEEPER SMASHER' ON IT!

THE 1882-83 CAMPAIGN, WHICH ENDED WITH A 6-1 THRASHING OF NEWCASTLE UPON TYNE, HAD SEEN CROWDS INCREASE, A RESERVE TEAM FORMED, AND ONLY 3 OUT OF 35 MATCHES LOST! HAVING FALLEN FOR FOOTBALL, THE NORTH END CLUB WERE NOW BECOMING RATHER GOOD AT IT.

MAY *1883*, THE DEEPDALE BRIDGE HOTEL.

THE NORTH END CRICKET AND FOOTBALL CLUB'S FLOURISHING STATE WAS CONFIRMED BY A LARGE ATTENDANCE AT THEIR ANNUAL MEETING.

BLACKBURN OLYMPIC FC. 1883 FA CHALLENGE CUP WINNERS.

HOPES WERE HIGH. BLACKBURN OLYMPIC HAD JUST BECOME THE FIRST NORTHERN TEAM TO WIN THE FA CUP, AND DESPITE THE CONSIDERABLE GAP BETWEEN THE TWO CLUBS, NORTH END'S FOOTBALL SECTION SAW THE PRESTIGE SUCH A WIN COULD BRING, AND THEY BEGAN TO DREAM OF SIMILAR SUCCESS.

AFTER A SUMPTUOUS MEAL, CLUB PRESIDENT MR W. E. M. TOMLINSON MP OFFERED SEVERAL TOASTS, INCLUDING ONE IN PRAISE OF QUEEN VICTORIA – *FOR HER CONTINUED SUPPORT OF ATHLETIC ENDEAVOUR!*

THE NIGHT WAS ALSO A CELEBRATION OF WILLIAM SUDELL'S *15* YEARS AT THE CLUB, AND OPENED WITH A SPECIAL GIFT FOR HIS WIFE...

ON BEHALF OF ALL OUR MEMBERS, PLEASE PRESENT THIS HANDSOME GIFT TO MRS SUDELL, AS TESTIMONY OF OUR FEELINGS FOR HER INTEREST IN OUR CLUB.

APPLAUSE AND MORE SPEECHES FOLLOWED, BEFORE AN ELABORATE GILT-FRAMED ADDRESS WAS PRESENTED TO WILLIAM SUDELL – IN THANKS FOR HIS GUIDANCE AND HARD WORK, AND AS AN EXPRESSION OF THE HIGH REGARD IN WHICH HE WAS HELD.

HEAR, HEAR!

SUDELL'S THANK-YOU SPEECH WAS EQUALLY FLORID...

FELLOW MEMBERS, I AM AGREEABLY SURPRISED AND GRATIFIED BY THE BEAUTY OF THIS ADDRESS...

...AND THANK YOU SINCERELY ON BEHALF OF MRS SUDELL FOR HER WONDERFUL GIFT.

THERE EXIST MANY MEMBERS HERE WHO HAVE WORKED JUST AS HARD AS I, AND DONE JUST AS GOOD A SERVICE. IF I STAND IN THIS PROMINENT POSITION IT IS ONLY BECAUSE ONE OF US MUST...

Preston North End Football Club

...INDEED, IF I MAY SAY TO YOU AS YOUR VICE-PRESIDENT, I WOULD MUCH RATHER SEE THIS CLUB STRIVE TO IMPROVE AND TO SUCCEED IN WINNING THE LANCASHIRE CUP- THAN FOR I TO RECEIVE A THOUSAND PRESENTS!

a modern Footbal club which can hold

WE HAVE BEEN THROUGH DARK TIMES AND HAVE NOW EMERGED INTO THE SUNSHINE! IF WE STICK TOGETHER WE SHALL ONE DAY GET TO LONDON AND IF WE DON'T WIN THE FA CUP, WE WILL BE VERY CLOSE TO DOING SO!

FOR HE'S A JOLLY GOOD FELLOW, FOR HE'S A JOLLY GOOD FELLOW, FOR HE'S A JOLLY GOOD FELLOW... AND SO SAY ALL OF US!

FIFTEEN YEARS AFTER JOINING THE CLUB AS A *16* YEAR OLD, WILLIAM SUDELL WAS PUBLICLY ENTRUSTED WITH ITS FUTURE.

NORTH END COULD NOT HAVE CHOSEN A MORE AMBITIOUS OR DETERMINED MAN.

CONSTRUCTION

By 'eck, 'tis a dangerous game!

IN THE SUMMER OF **1883**, QUEEN VICTORIA CELEBRATED **46** YEARS ON THE THRONE, WILLIAM GLADSTONE WAS BRITISH PRIME MINISTER, AND ONE YEAR ON FROM THE GUILD, THE LIVELY FOLK OF PRESTON WERE STILL BEING ENTERTAINED...

WILLIAM GLADSTONE

THE NEW GAIETY PALACE OF VARIETIES, ON TITHEBARN STREET, PRESENTED:

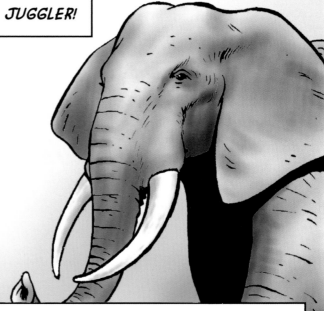

HERR ADALBERT FRIKELL, THE AMAZING CONJURER!

PRINCE, AERIAL EQUILIBRIST AND JUGGLER!

MISS SELINA SEAFORTH, CHAMPION FEMALE BOXER OF THE WORLD!

THE PLEASURE GARDENS OF NEW HALL LANE WERE ANOTHER ATTRACTION:

ACCLIMATISED PARROTS, FOR SALE.

JUMBO II, THE MAMMOTH ELEPHANT.

THEIR MANICURED LAWNS AND EXOTIC PLANTS PROVIDED WELCOME RELIEF FROM THE BRICKS AND SMOKE OF INDUSTRY.

THE GARDENS ALSO SHOWCASED REGULAR SPORTING EVENTS, AND PLAYED HOST TO NORTH END'S LOCAL FOOTBALLING RIVALS, PRESTON ZINGARI.

MINDFUL OF THE THREAT FROM LOCAL TEAMS, NORTH END WORKED HARD TO MAINTAIN THEIR STATUS AS THE TOWN'S ELITE CLUB.

OVER THE SUMMER THEY IMPROVED DEEPDALE BY PLACING RAILINGS AROUND THE FIELD AND ERECTING A NEW STAND, WHICH COULD HOUSE UP TO 600 SPECTATORS.

BY NOW NORTH END'S RUGBY TEAM HAD DISBANDED, AND FOOTBALL WAS FIRMLY INSTALLED AS THE NUMBER ONE SPORT. AND WITH CONSTRUCTION CARRIED OUT ON THE GROUND, WILLIAM SUDELL DECIDED TO BEGIN SOME BUILDING WORK OF HIS OWN.

"EVERYONE KNEW BILLY SUDELL, THE LIFE AND SPIRIT OF THE NORTH END." JIMMY CATTON.

BORN INTO A MIDDLE-CLASS FAMILY ON THE 17TH JULY 1850, BILLY WAS THE YOUNGEST OF 4 CHILDREN, WHOSE PROUD LINEAGE COULD BE TRACED BACK TO A GUILD MAYOR.

AS A CHILD, BILLY WAS PRIVATELY EDUCATED IN CHESHIRE, WHERE HE MIXED WITH CHILDREN FROM A HIGHER SOCIAL STANDING AND PURSUED HIS LOVE OF ALL THINGS SPORTING.

ALWAYS AN EXCELLENT SKATER, IT'S CLAIMED AT 12 YEARS OLD HE TRAVELLED THE ENTIRE LENGTH OF THE FROZEN PRESTON TO LANCASTER CANAL!

UPON RETURNING TO PRESTON, SUDELL BEGAN HIS WORKING LIFE WITH THE GOODAIRS – ONE OF THE MAJOR COTTON FAMILIES IN PRESTON.

DISPLAYING SOMETHING OF A GENIUS FOR FIGURES, HIS RISE WAS METEORIC AND HE PROGRESSED WITH EASE FROM CASHIER TO MANAGER AT JOHN GOODAIR'S, PEEL MILL IN DEEPDALE.

SOON THE GOODAIRS LOOKED UPON SUDELL AS ONE OF THEIR OWN, AND HIS WEALTH AND SOCIAL STATUS BLOSSOMED. AT THE HEIGHT OF HIS POWERS HE MOVED HIS WIFE AND THEIR 7 CHILDREN FROM AN ALREADY IMPRESSIVE ADDRESS ON ST. GEORGE'S TERRACE, DEEPDALE ROAD, TO THE EVEN GRANDER MOOR HOUSE OF HOLME SLACK.

HANNAY LIVERPOOL
317
N° 71

DELIGHTING IN SUDELL'S NETWORKING SKILLS, THE GOODAIRS ENCOURAGED HIM TO JOIN UP WITH THE LOCAL VOLUNTEERS FORCE AT FULWOOD BARRACKS. HERE HE WAS PROMOTED TO MAJOR — THE MONIKER BY WHICH HE WAS TO BECOME BEST KNOWN WITHIN THE FOOTBALL WORLD.

AT NORTH END, SUDELL THREW HIMSELF INTO THE CLUB...

WHEN HIS PLAYING DAYS ENDED, HE OFTEN PATROLLED THE GOAL LINE AS AN UMPIRE...

WHAT!

YES! GOAL!

...WITH ONLY A HINT OF BIAS!

A PROMINENT FORCE BEHIND THE MOVE TO DEEPDALE AND THE POPULAR ATHLETICS FESTIVALS, SUDELL HAD ABILITIES AND CONTACTS THAT SET HIM APART. OVER TIME HE BECAME THE CLUB'S NATURAL LEADER.

HIS AMBITIONS FOR NORTH END WERE LIMITLESS, AND COME THE SUMMER OF '83 HE NURTURED A DREAM — BOTH PURE IN HONESTY AND EXTREME IN VISION — *TO CREATE THE GREATEST FOOTBALL TEAM THE WORLD HAD EVER SEEN!*

BUT TO ACHIEVE THIS, HE WOULD HAVE TO CROSS THE BORDERS NOT JUST OF LANCASHIRE AND ENGLAND BUT THE LINES OF LEGALITY AND ACCEPTABILITY.

HIS QUEST BEGAN IN SCOTLAND.

WHEN MODERN FOOTBALL ARRIVED IN SCOTLAND, IT PROVED JUST AS POPULAR AS IN THE SOUTH, AND BY *1883* MANY CLUBS WERE ESTABLISHED.

AIRDRIE FC

RAITH ROVERS

RANGERS

EDINBURGH ST. BERNARD'S

JOHNSTONE

DUMBARTON

HEART OF MIDLOTHIAN

PARTICK THISTLE

THE FIRST MODERN CLUB WAS QUEEN'S PARK OF GLASGOW, WHO JOINED THE ENGLISH FA IN *1870*.

ONE OF ONLY *15* TEAMS TO ENTER THE INAUGURAL FA CUP IN *1872*, QUEEN'S PARK FAMOUSLY DONATED *1* GUINEA TOWARDS THE NEW TROPHY, AND WERE HANDED A BYE INTO THE SEMIS DUE TO THE LONG DISTANCES THEY'D HAVE TO TRAVEL.

THEY SHOCKED EVERYONE BY HOLDING THE FAVOURITES, WANDERERS, TO A *0-0* DRAW IN LONDON. HOWEVER, UNABLE TO AFFORD ANOTHER JOURNEY SOUTH, QUEEN'S PARK REFUSED A REPLAY, AND WANDERERS WENT ON TO WIN THE FINAL.

MONTHS LATER, IN NOVEMBER *1872*, THE FIRST EVER SCOTLAND v. ENGLAND INTERNATIONAL TOOK PLACE, IN PARTICK, GLASGOW.

THE GAME ENDED SCORELESS. BUT IN THE MATCHES THAT FOLLOWED, THE SCOTS (MOSTLY QUEEN'S PARK PLAYERS) INVARIABLY WON. WHY WAS THIS?
THE ANSWER WAS SIMPLE – THEY PASSED THE BALL. NOT LONG, HOOFED PASSES, BUT SHORT, CONSIDERED COMBINATIONS. ENGLAND'S PLAYERS, STUCK IN THEIR DRIBBLING AND CHARGING TRADITIONS, WERE BEING OUTCLASSED. QUEEN'S PARK'S THOUGHTFUL APPROACH, UNHINDERED BY OLD SCHOOL METHODS AND STUBBORN TACTICS, HAD TAKEN FOOTBALL TO A NEW LEVEL. EVERYONE ELSE WOULD HAVE TO CATCH UP.

SOUTH OF THE BORDER, IT DIDN'T TAKE LONG FOR CLUBS TO RECOGNISE THE BENEFITS OF HIRING SCOTTISH PLAYERS.

THE SCOTSMAN, OCTOBER 1882:

~~~ WANTED ~~~

FOOTBALL PLAYER (A good fullback)

Wanted for a club in northeast Lancashire, to act as Captain. To a really good man who can teach well, liberal wages will be given.

MANY CLUBS WERE NOW BEING RUN AS BUSINESSES, AND WITH THAT CAME THE PRESSURE TO SUCCEED. FOOTBALL WAS AN AMATEUR SPORT, YET ILLEGAL PAYMENTS TO PLAYERS HAD BEEN GOING ON FOR YEARS. THOSE 'EMPLOYING' PROFESSIONALS DID WHATEVER THEY COULD TO HOODWINK THE FA.

SHOW UP EARLY, LADS - THEN GO REST. YOU'RE NOT HERE FOR YOUR SPINNING SKILLS.

ACCOUNTS WERE FIDDLED. PAYMENTS IN KIND WERE MADE. FOOD AND ACCOMMODATION OFFERED. JOBS IN FACTORIES AND MILLS WERE SET UP WITH PLENTY OF TIME OFF TO PLAY FOOTBALL. IT WAS ALL A SCAM - AND EVERYONE KNEW IT.

FOR THE PLAYERS, A MOVE TO ENGLAND WAS NOT WITHOUT DRAWBACKS. TRAVEL WASN'T EASY, AND THEY WERE UNLIKELY TO SEE THEIR FRIENDS AND RELATIVES FOR A LONG TIME. IT WAS A HUGE COMMITMENT, YET THE PROSPECT OF BEING PAID TO PLAY FOOTBALL WAS HARD TO RESIST. MANY MADE THE TRIP SOUTH, WITH LANCASHIRE PROVING THE HOTTEST DESTINATION.

PERHAPS THE MOST FAMOUS 'PROFESSIONAL' IN LANCASHIRE WAS FERGIE SUTER, WHO JOINED DARWEN FROM PARTICK THISTLE IN 1878. A STONEMASON BY TRADE, FERGIE WAS HUGELY POPULAR WITH THE FANS, BUT LATER CAUSED CONTROVERSY BY SWITCHING TO FIERCE RIVALS BLACKBURN ROVERS AMIDST RUMOURS OF A £100 PAYMENT!

FERGIE SUTER

ONE 'UNDRED! I WOULDN'T JOIN THEM LOT FOR ONE THOUSAND!

I MIGHT.

AS MORE SCOTS FOLLOWED SUTER, THE SUCCESS OF THE LANCASHIRE CLUBS NATURALLY PROVOKED COMPLAINTS, AND IN *1882* THE FA TOOK A STANCE...

ALL PAYMENTS TO PLAYERS, EXCLUDING EXPENSES ARE **BANNED!**

ANY CLUB FOUND GUILTY WILL BE **EXPELLED** FROM THE ASSOCIATION!

THE FA WAS FORCED TO SET UP A SPECIAL COMMITTEE, BUT IT COULDN'T STEM THE TIDE. ETON'S DEFEAT TO BLACKBURN OLYMPIC IN THE '83 FA CUP FINAL WAS A WARNING SHOT. THE OLD BOYS' AMATEUR VALUES AND DOMINANCE WERE NOW UNDER SERIOUS THREAT FROM THE NORTH. FOOTBALL WAS A POWDER KEG WAITING TO EXPLODE, AND THE BRAZEN AMBITION OF BILLY SUDELL WAS ABOUT TO LIGHT THE FUSE.

SUDELL'S FIRST SIGNING THAT SUMMER WAS HIS MOST IMPORTANT.

NICHOLAS JOHN ROSS, AGED 20 - THE CAPTAIN OF HEART OF MIDLOTHIAN. A FLAGGER AND SLATER BY TRADE, ROSS WAS A SUPREMELY GIFTED PLAYER WITH A FEROCIOUS DESIRE TO WIN. IN ROSS, SUDELL RECOGNISED A KINDRED SPIRIT AND THE PLAYER HE COULD BUILD HIS TEAM AROUND.

GEORGE 'GEORDIE' DRUMMOND, AGED 23 - JOINED FROM EDINBURGH ST. BERNARD'S. HIGHLY RECOMMENDED BY NEW SIGNING NICK ROSS, GEORDIE WAS A PRIZE-WINNING SPRINTER WITH THE ABILITY TO PLAY IN ANY POSITION HE FANCIED!

DAVID 'DAVIE' RUSSELL, AGED 21 - JOINED FROM STEWARTON CUNNINGHAME. HAILING FROM THE SAME VILLAGE AS NORTH END FORWARD JOHN BELGER, DAVIE HAD FOOTBALLING SKILLS TO MATCH HIS VIBRANT PERSONALITY. AND AS AN ASPIRING MUSIC HALL ARTISTE AND COMEDIAN, HE WAS ALWAYS GOOD FOR TEAM MORALE!

HA HA!

HA HA!

A NEW KIT ARRIVED TOO!

ANOTHER ADDITION TO THE RANKS WAS GEORGE WILSON, WHO PROVOKED OUTRAGE BY JOINING NORTH END FROM CUP-WINNING BLACKBURN OLYMPIC! A TOP SCORER FOR OLYMPIC, WILSON WAS ENTICED TO DEEPDALE BY THE PROSPECT OF BECOMING LANDLORD AT THE BLACK-A-MOOR HEAD INN ON LANCASTER ROAD. OLYMPIC FANS WERE EVEN MORE INCENSED WHEN THEY HEARD WILSON WAS TO BE MARRIED IN PRESTON!

THEY OFFERED WILSON A PUB - HE COULDN'T SAY NO!

LUCKY FELLER. HE'S GETTIN' MARRIED NOW AN' ALL.

SURELY THEY DIDN'T GET HIM A WIFE AS WELL AS A PUB?!

EVENIN'!

THE 1883-84 SEASON GOT UNDERWAY.

NORTH END'S NEW DAWN OPENED WITH DRAWS AGAINST DARWEN AND ACCRINGTON, THEN A LOSS IN A RETURN MATCH WITH DARWEN. IT WASN'T UNTIL A VISIT TO OLD CONQUERORS TURTON THAT SUDELL'S NEW-LOOK TEAM BEGAN TO SHOW WHAT IT COULD DO.

ON SATURDAY EVENING, FANS READ THE MATCH REPORT ON THE WINDOW OF THE *PRESTON HERALD*'S OFFICE...

A STRING OF WINS FOLLOWED, AND NORTH END GREW IN STATURE. THEY BEGAN SEEKING TEAMS FROM OUTSIDE OF LANCASHIRE, AND SOON CAME TO THE ATTENTION OF ONE OF THE FINEST AROUND - THE FAMOUS WEST BROMWICH ALBION.

IN OCTOBER 1883, WEST BROM ARRIVED AT DEEPDALE.

NORTH END: JOY, DUCKWORTH, ROBINSON, WILSON, RUSSELL, BROWN, ROSS, DRUMMOND, BELGER, DEWHURST, SMALLEY.

HE'S BEAT 'EM ALL!

25 MINUTES IN, BELGER WENT ON A TYPICAL RUN.

HE CROSSED TO ROSS...

YEESSSSS!

1-0!

UGHH!

BELGER AND DEWHURST ADDED TWO MORE, AND A GOOD-TEMPERED MATCH ENDED 3-1 TO PNE!

HURRAY!

CLAP!

CLAP!

THE FANS APPLAUDED BOTH TEAMS OFF THE PITCH.

THE MUTUAL APPRECIATION CONTINUED AT THE AFTER-MATCH DINNER...

TO THE GOOD HEALTH OF WEST BROMWICH ALBION!

WEST BROM'S DOCTOR REPLIED, SOMEWHAT PROPHETICALLY...

THIS IS BY FAR THE BEST AND MOST PLEASANT MATCH WE'VE PLAYED IN, AND I HOPE WE MEET IN THE ENGLISH CUP FINAL, TO BATTLE IT OUT AGAIN!

HEAR, HEAR!

AMIDST THE CONTINUING MERRIMENT, TWO PLAYERS WENT MISSING...

HERE THEY ARE!

NICE APRONS, LADS?!

GIGGLE!

TO BE FOUND LATER IN THE SCULLERY!

THE FUN DIDN'T STOP THERE, AS THE GANG PROGRESSED TO A HOTEL IN TOWN...

♪ FOR AULD LANG SYNE... ♫

REALLY ALFRED! AT THIS HOUR!

THE EVENING'S CELEBRATIONS MADE ALMOST AS MUCH NEWS AS THE MATCH ITSELF, AND GAINED THE PLAYERS A CERTAIN REPUTATION.

WEEKS LATER, COME SATURDAY 1ST DECEMBER, MINDS WERE FIRMLY BACK ON FOOTBALL AS NORTH END FACED A NEW CHALLENGE. HAVING WON 9 OUT OF 13 GAMES, CONFIDENCE WAS HIGH, YET A NEW KIND OF TENSION SURROUNDED THE DAY'S GAME. WITH A BUMPER CROWD EXPECTED AND A SPECIAL EXCITEMENT IN THE AIR, IT COULD MEAN ONLY ONE THING - *THE FA CUP WAS COMING TO DEEPDALE!*

DEBARRED

ICE CREAM!

HAVING RECEIVED A BYE IN ROUND **1**, NORTH END KICKED OFF THEIR FIRST EVER FA CUP TIE IN ROUND **2** AT HOME TO GREAT LEVER OF BOLTON.

THE GAME BEGAN IN SPECTACULAR FASHION...

NORTH END MADE A MIGHTY RUSH DOWNHILL TOWARDS LEVER'S GOAL.

A PILE-UP ENSUED...

HIT THE LEATHER!

AND DRUMMOND SCORED IN THE FIRST MINUTE! *WHAT A START!*

THREE MORE GOALS SENT NORTH END INTO THE NEXT ROUND!

THE MATCH REPORT IN THE *HERALD* GAVE SPECIAL MENTION TO THE NORTH END SUPPORT:

YESS!

FINAL SCORE: 4-1

Prestonians are fast learning to take a most engrossing interest in Association football, and as proof of this we point to the immense gathering of spectators at Deepdale on Saturday - nearly 8,000 - composed of all sorts and conditions of men:

...rich and poor,

...high and low,

...employers and employed,

...saints and sinners,

...everyone taking an almost overwhelming interest in a manly English game.

NORTH END'S GROWING AND ECLECTIC FAN BASE WAS BEGINNING TO EARN AS MUCH COVERAGE AS THE TEAM ITSELF! AND ON CHRISTMAS DAY THEY QUITE LITERALLY REACHED NEW HEIGHTS...

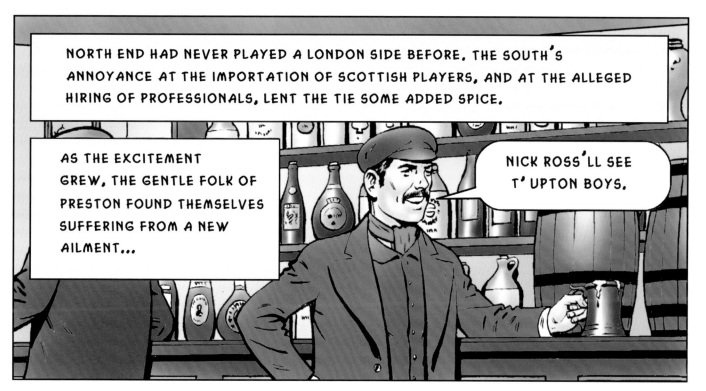

NORTH END HAD NEVER PLAYED A LONDON SIDE BEFORE. THE SOUTH'S ANNOYANCE AT THE IMPORTATION OF SCOTTISH PLAYERS, AND AT THE ALLEGED HIRING OF PROFESSIONALS, LENT THE TIE SOME ADDED SPICE.

AS THE EXCITEMENT GREW, THE GENTLE FOLK OF PRESTON FOUND THEMSELVES SUFFERING FROM A NEW AILMENT...

NICK ROSS'LL SEE T' UPTON BOYS.

BELGER'S THE FELLOW TO PUT THE WIND UP 'EM.

HE'S NO SHORTAGE OF TRICKERY, EITHER.

THREE OR FOUR, LUV?

EH? 'AM SURE WE'LL SCORE MORE THAN THREE!

...CUP FEVER!

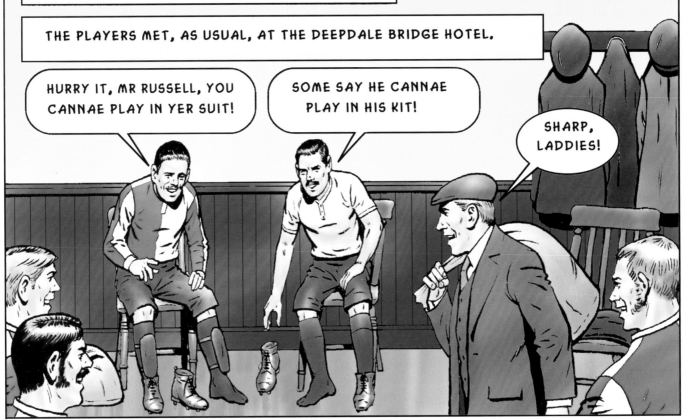

SATURDAY 19TH JANUARY, 1884. MATCH DAY.

THE PLAYERS MET, AS USUAL, AT THE DEEPDALE BRIDGE HOTEL.

THEN MADE THE WALK ALONG DEEPDALE ROAD TOWARDS THE GROUND.

OUTSIDE THE GROUND, DEEPDALE ROAD WAS LINED WITH ALL MANNER OF PALATABLE TREATS TO TEMPT THE FANS.

WHILST INSIDE THE ENCLOSURE THE 'PAYBOXES' HAD NEVER BEEN SO BUSY.

IT APPEARED THE WHOLE OF PRESTON HAD DESCENDED UPON DEEPDALE!

UPTON FOUGHT BACK.

AND SHOWED GREAT SKILL...

BRAVO!

BUT DUCKWORTH...

ROSS...

NNNF!

AND JOY...

HELD FIRM.

HOWEVER, IN THE SECOND HALF, UPTON WON A FREE KICK FOR 'HANDS', AND...

NOOOOO!

FINAL SCORE: 1-1.

BOTH TEAMS WERE EXHAUSTED, BUT MUCH TO THE DELIGHT OF THE CROWD, AGREED TO PLAY 30 MINUTES OF EXTRA TIME.

DURING EXTRA TIME, NORTH END HAD ALL THE PLAY, AND CONTINUALLY BOMBARDED THEIR VISITOR'S GOAL...

UNTIL EVENTUALLY...

GOAL!

DEEPDALE CELEBRATED LIKE NEVER BEFORE!

BUT DESPERATE UPTON OFFICIALS CONFRONTED THE REFEREE...

AND AFTER MUCH CONSIDERATION...

NO GOAL - OFFSIDE!

IT WAS THE SECOND NORTH END GOAL TO BE DISALLOWED, AND THE FANS VENTED THEIR ANGER TOWARDS REFEREE T. HINDLE.

THE EPIC ENCOUNTER ENDED 1-1. NORTH END HAD FORCED 18 CORNERS; UPTON PARK, ONLY ONE. LATER, UPTON GAVE THANKS FOR AN *AGREEABLE VISIT NORTH,* AND WITH GOOD GRACE ADMITTED NORTH END WERE THE BETTER SIDE. NORTH END DULY PRESENTED UPTON WITH THEIR SHARE OF THE GATE, £81.00 - AND WITH THE CLUBS ON GOOD TERMS, TALKS BEGAN ON STAGING A REPLAY.

HOWEVER, THE VERY NEXT DAY, NORTH END RECEIVED SHATTERING NEWS...

ON SUNDAY MORNING, CLUB SECRETARY BETHEL ROBINSON RECEIVED A LETTER FROM THE FOOTBALL ASSOCIATION IN LONDON.

WHAT?!

Dear Sir

I beg to inform you that I have this morning received a protest from the Upton Park Club against your club on the grounds of professionalism. It will be placed before the committee at their next meeting. Yours truly C. W. Alcock Hon. Secretary.

NORTH END HAD BEEN ACCUSED OF BREAKING FA RULE NO. 15.

15. Any member of a club receiving remuneration or consideration of any sort above his actual expenses, and any wages actually lost by any such player taking part in any match, shall be debarred from taking part in either Cup, Inter Association, or International contests, and any club employing such player shall be excluded from this Association.

ON THE EVENING OF SATURDAY 26TH JANUARY, A NORTH END COMMITTEE ARRIVED AT KENNINGTON OVAL, LONDON, TO APPEAR BEFORE THE FA.

WILLIAM SUDELL WAS CROSS-EXAMINED FOR ALMOST 2 HOURS, YET NEITHER THE CLUB'S SECRETARY NOR ITS TREASURER WERE CALLED.

SUDELL FREELY ADMITTED TO IMPORTING PLAYERS AND FINDING THEM JOBS, BUT DISAGREED THAT THE CLUB HAD BREACHED RULE 15.

AFTER MUCH DELIBERATION A DECISION WAS REACHED - PRESIDENT MARINDIN PRAISED SUDELL FOR HIS *FRANK AND STRAIGHTFORWARD MANNER,* BUT NEVERTHELESS...

"PRESTON NORTH END ARE DEBARRED FROM THIS YEAR'S FA CHALLENGE CUP, BUT SHALL REMAIN A MEMBER OF THE ASSOSIATION."

FLAMIN' 'ECK! WE'VE BEEN *THROWN OUT!*

WHAT?!

IT WAS A SOMEWHAT STRANGE DECISION BY THE FA. NO ACTUAL EVIDENCE AGAINST NORTH END WAS PRODUCED, AND THE FA EVEN REFUSED TO VIEW THEIR BOOKS.

THE NEWS INFURIATED LANCASHIRE'S CLUBS, WHO VIEWED IT AS AN UNFAIR ATTACK FROM THE METROPOLIS, AND IT LEFT THEM CONCERNED AS TO WHAT MAY HAPPEN NEXT - FOR AS A LETTER IN *THE HERALD* POINTED OUT:

...most of Lancashire's clubs hire professionals, indeed, Bolton Wanderers have 14, Halliwell 10, Burnley 8, Accrington 7, and Blackburn Rovers and Blackburn Olympic have 3 each!

MORE CONTROVERSY FOLLOWED. WHEN NORTH END WERE IN LONDON, IT WAS REPORTED THEY WERE SHOWN EVERY KINDNESS BY THE UPTON PARK COMMITTEE, WHO DENIED HAVING MADE ANY PROTEST!

SO WHO DID MAKE THE COMPLAINT? THE FANS AND NEWSPAPERS WERE QUICK TO LIST THEIR SUSPECTS...

IF IT WEREN'T UPTON LADS, IT'LL BE SOME OTHER LONDON CLUB – THEY RESENT OUR SUCCESS.

I READ, AN FA OFFICIAL HAS BEEN GATHERING EVIDENCE IN SCOTLAND FOR SOME TIME, AFTER COMPLAINTS FROM HEARTS AND ST. BERNARDS.

MY GUESS, 'TIS LOCAL. I ASK THEE, WOT LANKY CLUB GAINS MOST 'AVIN' US OUTA PICTURE?

WELL... IT WASN'T... ME...

WHOEVER RAISED THE COMPLAINT HAD UPSET THE HORNET'S NEST. ALTHOUGH ACCRINGTON HAD PREVIOUSLY BEEN CALLED TO ACCOUNT BY THE FA, NORTH END WERE A DIFFERENT PROSPECT, AND THE LONG-SIMMERING ROW OVER PROFESSIONALISM WAS NOW AT BOILING POINT.

OVER AT DEEPDALE THE MOOD WAS RESOLUTE. WITH SO MUCH INVESTED, THE FUTURE *HAD* TO BE PROFESSIONAL – AND SUDELL AND THE NORTH END COMMITTEE WOULD DO EVERYTHING IN THEIR POWER TO MAKE IT SO. THEIR CRY WAS SIMPLE – WE MAY HAVE LOST THIS BATTLE, BUT WE'LL YET WIN THE WAR!

CHANGE

This threatens our very existence!

OUT OF THE CUP, NORTH END SOUGHT TO APPEASE DISAPPOINTED FANS BY ARRANGING FIXTURES WITH THE BEST TEAMS AROUND – AND A HOME MATCH AGAINST ARCH RIVALS BLACKBURN ROVERS CERTAINLY FITTED THE BILL.

MEMORIES OF HEAVY DEFEATS STILL LINGERED, AND WITH SOME SECTIONS SUGGESTING ROVERS WERE BEHIND THE 'UPTON PARK LETTER', THE MATCH WAS VIEWED AS A CHANCE FOR REVENGE.

SATURDAY 24TH FEB, 1884 – THOUSANDS OF ROVERS FANS ARRIVED BY TRAIN.

TO CAPITALISE ON THEIR RECENT BIG CROWDS, ANOTHER GRANDSTAND – THIS ONE MEASURING 48 YARDS LONG – WAS BUILT ALONGSIDE THE EXISTING ONE.

BOTH STANDS COMBINED COULD HOLD UP TO **2,000** SPECTATORS, AND ONE HOUR BEFORE KICK-OFF THEY WERE ALREADY FULL!

NORTH END WERE LOUDLY APPLAUDED ONTO THE FIELD. BUT IT WAS ANOTHER **20** MINUTES BEFORE THE ROVERS TEAM APPEARED!

NICE OF 'EM TO SHOW!

THE PITCH WAS BOGGY AFTER RECENT STORMS...

ACH!

BUT NORTH END HAD THE BEST OF THE EARLY PLAY, AND...

AFTER JUST **10** MINUTES...

1 - 0!

SMASHER!

JACK GORDON MADE IT **2-0** BEFORE HALF-TIME. THEN, IN THE **2ND** HALF...

NNNF!

WYLIE HEADED...

AND GORDON FOLLOWED UP!

YEESSS!

AT 3-0, THE GAME LOOKED OVER – BUT WAS IT?

JUST ONE MINUTE LATER –
JOY SLIPPED IN THE MUD...

COME ON!

3 - 1!

AND THEN BROWN DRIBBLED
THROUGH THE NORTH END DEFENCE...

THERE'S ANOTHER!

3 - 2!

TENSIONS BEGAN TO MOUNT...

OOOOF!

REFEREE?!

AFTER A ROUGH CHALLENGE, LOFTHOUSE
SQUARED UP TO DRUMMOND!

EASY, LADDIES!

BUT NORTH END HELD ON, AND
WERE DESERVED WINNERS!

YES!

TO HAVE FINALLY BEATEN ROVERS WAS A GREAT
FEELING FOR THE NORTH END FAITHFUL...

WE'D 'AVE
WON THAT
CUP, NAY
BOTHER!

THEER BE
NO DOUBTIN'
US NOW!

IT WAS ALSO A SPECIAL MOMENT FOR THE
CLUB, AND VINDICATED WILLIAM SUDELL'S
RECENT SIGNINGS.

SINCE THE SUMMER, SUDELL HAD CONTINUED TO STRENGTHEN THE TEAM.

ALEX 'SANDY' ROBERTSON, A PAINTER BY TRADE, SIGNED FROM EDIN. ST. BERNARD'S.

JOHNNY 'JACK' GRAHAM, A FORMER QUARRYMAN. NICKNAME: SAFETY VALVE!

JOHN 'JACK' GORDON, A JOINER IN LEYLAND, PLAYED FOR OLD PORT GLASGOW.

SAM THOMSON, A VERSATILE FORWARD FROM GLASGOW RANGERS.

JAMES D. ROSS, YOUNGER BROTHER OF NICK ROSS, 5 FT 7, AND A LETHAL FORWARD.

ROBERT 'BOB' HOWARTH, BORN IN PRESTON! PROMOTED FROM THE RESERVES.

THE 'BACKROOM' TEAM WAS ALSO TAKING SHAPE. AT THE CLUB'S AGM IN MARCH '84 – HELD AT THE BLACK-A-MOOR'S HEAD – SUDELL WAS RE-ELECTED CHAIRMAN, W. E. M. TOMLINSON MP, PRESIDENT, AND THOMAS BANKS, TREASURER.

BETHEL ROBINSON AND FRED DEWHURST WERE DECLARED CLUB SECRETARIES, AND A COMMITTEE OF 12 DRAWN UP, WHICH INCLUDED NAMES FROM THE OLD CRICKETING DAYS: J. WOODS, W. NAYLOR, W. POMFRET, W. TURNER, W.H. HULME, J. PARKINSON, H. S. CARTMELL, R. GREEN, F. WOODS, W. WHITESIDE, J. SUMNER AND J. MILNER.

DURING THE MARCH AGM, AMIDST ARGUMENTS OVER EXPENSES, IT WAS ANNOUNCED THAT £332 HAD BEEN SPENT ON NEW STANDS - AND IN LATE SUMMER THAT YEAR, FURTHER IMPROVEMENTS WERE CARRIED OUT AT DEEPDALE.

A 'DRESSING TENT' WAS CONSTRUCTED IN THE NORTH-WEST CORNER OF THE GROUND. CONTAINING 4 LARGE BATHS AND COSTING £200, THE NEW TENT MEANT THE DAYS OF CHANGING IN THE DEEPDALE BRIDGE HOTEL WERE OVER.

ALONG WITH THE TENT, THE GRANDSTANDS RECEIVED A LICK OF PAINT, AND A CINDER PATH WAS LAID OFF DEEPDALE ROAD TO PROVIDE BETTER ACCESS INTO THE ENCLOSURE.

AND IT WAS NOW, WITH DEEPDALE PRIMED AND SHIPSHAPE, THAT NORTH END DECLARED THEIR WITHDRAWAL FROM THE FA CUP FOR THE COMING '84-85 SEASON.

SINCE BEING KICKED OUT OF THE PREVIOUS FA CUP, WILLIAM SUDELL HAD BEEN WORKING STEALTHILY - DETERMINED TO SEE PROFESSIONALISM LEGALISED.

GENTLEMEN, PROFESSIONALISM *IS* INEVITABLE...

FOOTBALL IS CHANGING...

FAR BETTER FOR THE FA TO CONTROL THESE CHANGES - THAN LOSE ALL CONTROL IN THE FUTURE!

USING ALL HIS CHARM AND SOCIAL CUNNING, HE'D GAINED VALUABLE SUPPORT AND MADE SOME POWERFUL, AND SURPRISING, ALLIES...

CHARLES ALCOCK
FA SECRETARY.

ARTHUR KINNAIRD
FA TREASURER AND
OLD ETONIAN.

DR EDWARD MORLEY
CHAIRMAN OF
BLACKBURN ROVERS.

ALL THREE WERE STAUNCH SUPPORTERS OF THE AMATEUR IDEAL — YET SUDELL'S ARGUMENT WAS PERSUASIVE ENOUGH FOR THEM TO REALISE THAT PROFESSIONALISM REALLY WAS INEVITABLE. YET THERE REMAINED MANY OPPONENTS, WHO INCLUDED ALONG WITH THE SOUTHERN TEAMS, CLUBS FROM BIRMINGHAM, NOTTINGHAM AND SHEFFIELD.

THE CRUX OF THE PROBLEM LAY IN THE CLASS DIVIDE. AMATEUR PLAYERS FROM MIDDLE OR UPPER-CLASS BACKGROUNDS DIDN'T NEED TO PLAY OR, IN SOME CASES, EVEN WORK FOR MONEY. IN FACT, MANY AMATEURS THOUGHT IT IMMORAL TO PLAY SPORT FOR A LIVING — YET HERE MORE THAN A HINT OF HYPOCRISY EXISTED, FOR THEY WOULD CLAIM LARGE AMOUNTS ON EXPENSES. BUT ULTIMATELY, THEY FEARED THAT THE WORKING-CLASS PROFESSIONALS WOULD TAKE CONTROL OF 'THEIR' GAME — AND THE BURGEONING SUCCESS OF THE NORTHERN CLUBS ONLY HEIGHTENED THOSE FEARS.

THE *FOOTBALL FIELD* MAGAZINE CARRIED THE ARGUMENT...

LET THOSE WHO SNEER AT FOOTBALL PROFESSIONALISM OVER THEIR WALNUTS AND WINE, CONSIDER FOR A MOMENT, WHAT IT IS FOR A WORKING MAN WHO HAS TO BE THROWN ON HIS OWN RESOURCES.

BY 'ECK!

I QUITE LIKE WALNUTS.

CHANGE WAS AFOOT. ALL OVER BRITAIN SOCIAL REFORMS WERE TAKING PLACE — AND SUDELL AND THE NORTHERN CLUBS BELIEVED FOOTBALL SHOULD BE NO EXCEPTION.

IN OCTOBER, THE FA ISSUED A CIRCULAR ORDERING MEMBERS TO SUPPLY LISTS OF IMPORTED PLAYERS AND THEIR WAGES.

THIS THREATENS OUR VERY EXISTENCE! I DO NOT WANT TO BE TOLD HOW TO RUN MY CLUB ANY LONGER!

THE NORTHERNERS REACTED - 7 CLUBS WITHDREW FROM THE FA CUP, AND SUDELL CHAIRED A SERIES OF MEETINGS ABOUT THE FORMATION OF A BREAKAWAY ASSOCIATION FOR PROFESSIONAL CLUBS.

BURNLEY, BOLTON WANDERERS, ASTON VILLA AND SUNDERLAND WERE AMONGST THE LEADING CLUBS WHO ATTENDED THE MEETINGS - BUT NO CONCRETE DECISION ON A NEW ASSOCIATION WAS MADE.

HOWEVER, THE THREAT OF A BREAKAWAY WAS ENOUGH TO FORCE THE FA INTO ACTION, AND, AFTER FORMING A SUB-COMMITTEE, THEY FINALLY RECOMMENDED THE LEGALISATION OF PROFESSIONALISM! BUT TO BECOME FA POLICY IT NEEDED A VOTE - WITH A TWO-THIRDS MAJORITY REQUIRED.

AS THE DRAMA UNFOLDED OFF THE PITCH, NORTH END CONTINUED TO IMPRESS ON IT, BUT IN DECEMBER '84, A NEW TRAGEDY STRUCK. AFTER RETURNING FROM A LONG ILLNESS, CROWD HERO AND PROLIFIC SCORER JOHN BELGER BROKE HIS RIGHT LEG IN A CLASH AGAINST GREAT LEVER, AND SADLY HIS REMARKABLE CAREER WAS OVER.

A SPECIAL COLLECTION WAS RAISED, AND *FOOTBALL FIELD* REMARKED:

...Preston folk have too great an affection for the members of their almost invincible team, to behave towards them in anything but a handsome manner.

GO ON, SMASHER!

JOHN BELGER HOBBLED OUT OF PRESTON NORTH END AND WALKED STRAIGHT INTO THEIR HISTORY, AS PERHAPS THE CLUB'S FIRST TRULY GREAT PLAYER.

AFTER THE RECOMMENDATION OF THE FA SUB-COMMITTEE, A DATE AND PLACE WERE SET FOR THE VOTE. FITTINGLY, THE VENUE WAS THE FREEMASONS' TAVERN IN LONDON - SCENE OF THE FA'S FORMATION IN *1863!* OVER *200* DELEGATES ATTENDED FROM CLUBS AROUND THE COUNTRY, INCLUDING, FROM PRESTON: FISHWICK RAMBLERS, HIGHER WALTON AND PRESTON ZINGARI.

MAJOR MARINDIN TOOK THE CHAIR, AND CHARLES ALCOCK PROPOSED THE MOTION - BRINGING MUCH BOOING FROM THE MIDLAND AND SOUTHERN CLUBS.

BRAVO!

CHARLES CRUMP, PRESIDENT OF THE BIRMINGHAM FA, SPOKE UP...

THE INTRODUCTION OF PROFESSIONALISM WILL BE THE RUIN OF THE PASTIME!

HEAR, HEAR!

AS DID HARRY CHAMBERS, A FOUNDER OF THE ORIGINAL SHEFFIELD CLUB...

LANCASHIRE IS A JOHNNY-COME-LATELY TO FOOTBALL, AND HAS NO RIGHT TO DICTATE ITS VIEWS TO THE REST OF THE COUNTRY!

THEN, TO A RAPTUROUS RECEPTION, WILLIAM SUDELL, CHIEF PROMOTER OF PROFESSIONALISM, TOOK TO THE FLOOR...

GENTLEMEN, PRESTON ARE ALL PROFESSIONALS, BUT IF YOU REFUSE TO LEGALISE THEM THEY WILL ALL BE AMATEURS.

WE SHALL ALL BE AMATEURS, AND YOU CANNOT PROVE US OTHERWISE!

HURRAH!

TWO AND A HALF HOURS LATER, THE VOTE TOOK PLACE...

FOR: 113, AGAINST: 108.

A WIN, BUT SHORT OF THE TWO-THIRDS MAJORITY.

TWO MONTHS LATER, A SECOND VOTE FAILED TO REACH THE MAJORITY, BUT SUPPORT WAS RISING, AND WITH VICTORY IN SIGHT, ANOTHER SUB-COMMITTEE - THIS TIME CONTAINING WILLIAM SUDELL - WAS SET UP TO PUSH THE VOTE HOME.

FINALLY, ON THE 20TH JULY 1885, AFTER ONLY 47 DELEGATES ATTENDED ANDERTON'S HOTEL TO CAST THEIR VOTES...

VOTES, FOR... 35!

MOTION PASSED!

Professionals:
Professionals shall be allowed to compete in all Cup games, provided that they are qualified as follows:
In Cup matches: by birth or residence for two years past, within six miles of the ground, or headquarters of the club for which they play.

THE LANCASHIRE AND NORTHERN CLUBS HAD GAINED A HISTORIC VICTORY, AND THE FUTURE OF MODERN FOOTBALL WAS CHANGED FOREVER.

HERO OF THE HOUR, WILLIAM SUDELL, WAS DULY GRANTED A PLACE ON THE NEW FA COMMITTEE - CEMENTING HIS STATUS AS ONE OF THE MOST POWERFUL MEN IN FOOTBALL.

HE'D WON HIS WAR, AND WAS AT LAST FREE TO CONTINUE HIS QUEST - AND TAKE NORTH END TO THE TOP OF THE FOOTBALL WORLD.

ON THE ROAD

GET 'IM!
RUN!

AS SUDELL CHASED PERFECTION ON THE PITCH, HE URGED HIS PLAYERS TO BECOME STUDENTS OF THE GAME, AND CONTINUED TO USE INVENTIVE COACHING METHODS.

CHESS PIECES WERE USED TO EXPLAIN FORMATIONS.

IN THE ABSENCE OF JOHN BELGER, NICK ROSS WAS PROMOTED TO CAPTAIN AND BECAME SUDELL'S 'VOICE' ON THE PITCH. KNOWN AS THE 'DEMON BACK', ROSS'S FIERCE REPUTATION BELIED HIS ASTUTE MIND AND BROAD TACTICAL KNOWLEDGE, AND FROM FULL BACK HE WAS IDEALLY PLACED TO READ AND MARSHAL THE TEAM.

ANOTHER 'THINKER' OF THE SIDE WAS RECENT ADDITION JOHN GOODALL, SIGNED FROM GREAT LEVER, GOODALL WAS SHARP AS A TACK, AND HIS THOUGHTFUL STYLE COMPLEMENTED NORTH END'S SCIENTIFIC APPROACH.

INSPIRED BY QUEEN'S PARK'S FORMATION AND SHORT-PASSING GAME, NORTH END REFINED IT BY DROPPING ONE FORWARD BACK INTO THE MIDDLE – THUS CREATING A MORE COMPACT SHAPE.

NICK ROSS DEVELOPED THE BACK PASS...

YOURS, BILLY!

USING GOALKEEPER BILLY ROSE AS AN EXTRA DEFENDER.

HEADING, USUALLY A DEFENSIVE ACT, WAS DEPLOYED IN ATTACK...

GERRUP, FRED!

AND THE PINPOINT CROSSES OF JACK GORDON YIELDED A RICH HARVEST FOR NORTH END'S FORWARDS.

WHILST THE STRONG ARMS OF JACK GRAHAM...

WHAT A THROW!

...PROVED JUST AS ACCURATE AS A GORDON CROSS!

ALL THESE INNOVATIONS MADE NORTH END EXCITING TO WATCH. YET HOME CROWDS HAD BEGUN TO FLUCTUATE.

WITH SO MANY GAMES PLAYED AT DEEPDALE, HARD-UP FANS WERE SELECTIVE ABOUT WHICH THEY ATTENDED – AND WITH MOST OF DEEPDALE OPEN TO THE ELEMENTS, PRESTON'S CLIMATE ALSO PLAYED A PART!

WE MUST BE MAD!

OUTSIDE OF PRESTON, NORTH END'S FAME CONTINUED TO GROW. NOTORIOUS FOR THE UPTON PARK FALL-OUT AND SUDELL'S BATTLES, IT SEEMED EVERYBODY WANTED TO SEE THE *PROFESSIONALS* PLAY – AND WITH HOME CROWDS FLUCTUATING, **THE PRESTON NORTH END SHOW** HIT THE ROAD!

WHILST ON THEIR TRAVELS, NORTH END (NOW SPORTING STRIPES) WOULD OFTEN BE MOCKED FOR THEIR 'FOREIGN' CONTINGENT.

AT NOTTS COUNTY...

OWER TAE ME, LADDIE!

WHAT A STWANGE ACCENT THESE LANCASHIRE FELLAS HAVE?

IT'S AWFULLY LIKE SCOTCH!

BUT IT DIDN'T BOTHER THE PLAYERS – WHO JUST KEPT ON SCORING!

♪ THREE GYPSIES CAM TAE OOR HALL DOOR... ♪

♪ AND OH, BUT THEY SANG BONNY OHHH! ♪

HAVING RETURNED TO THE FA CUP COMPETITION FOR THE 85-86 SEASON, NORTH END REACHED THE 3RD ROUND, WHERE THEY TRAVELLED TO BOLTON WANDERERS' PIKES LANE GROUND IN DECEMBER – AND CAME AWAY WITH A 3-2 VICTORY! BUT THEN, HISTORY REPEATED ITSELF...

NOT AGAIN!

BOLTON REPORTED NORTH END FOR FIELDING GEORDIE DRUMMOND – WHO'D BROKEN THE *RESIDENCY RULE*, AFTER A BRIEF WORKING VISIT BACK IN HIS HOMETOWN OF EDINBURGH.

NATURALLY, SUDELL RETALIATED, AND BOLTON WERE ALSO THROWN OUT FOR FIELDING AN INELIGIBLE PLAYER!

STILL, IT WAS NO CONSOLATION FOR NORTH END. MISSING OUT ONCE MORE ON THEIR MOST COVETED PRIZE, THEY AGAIN HAD TO REVIVE THEIR SEASON BY ENTICING THE BEST TO DEEPDALE. AND THERE WAS ONE TEAM ABOVE ALL WHO COULD RIGHTFULLY CHALLENGE SUDELL'S BOAST OF BEING THE BEST IN THE WORLD...

CORINTHIANS

FOUNDED IN *1882* BY NICHOLAS L. 'PA' JACKSON, CORINTHIANS WAS A CLUB OF ENGLISH AMATEURS, FORMED TO AID THE NATIONAL SIDE'S BATTLES AGAINST THE EVER-DOMINANT SCOTS. HAND-PICKED FROM THE COUNTRY'S FINEST, THESE PROUD CHAMPIONS OF THE AMATEUR CODE REFUSED TO ENTER CUP COMPETITIONS AND INSTEAD TOURED BRITAIN, CHALLENGING THE BEST TEAMS AROUND.

MIGHTY STRUGGLES WITH NORTH END HAD ALREADY TAKEN PLACE, AND ON SATURDAY *19*TH DECEMBER *1885*, CORINTHIANS ENTERED DEEPDALE WITH 9 INTERNATIONALS AND A FIERCE DETERMINATION TO AVENGE THEIR LAST DEFEAT AT THE HANDS, OR RATHER FEET, OF SUDELL'S MEN.

NO MISTAKES TODAY, GENTLEMEN.

IT WAS A MATCH THE *10,000* FANS WOULD NEVER FORGET.

JUST 25 MINUTES IN, NORTH END WERE 0-2 DOWN!

BUT THEY STAGED A DRAMATIC COMEBACK, AND SOON LEVELLED THANKS TO FRED DEWHURST AND A SCRIMMAGED TEAM EFFORT! THEN ROBERTSON LOFTED IN A CORNER...

DEWHURST!

3 - 2!

BUT, INCREDIBLY, ON THE STROKE OF HALF-TIME...

UGGHH!

ROSE WAS FLOORED...

AND...

3 - 3!

I CAN'T TAKE ANY MORE!

BUT IN THE SECOND HALF, IT WAS ALL NORTH END, AND ON 80 MINUTES...

DEWHURST GOT *THE WINNER!*

4 - 3!

AFTERWARDS, A CORINTHIAN SPORTINGLY CONCEDED – *WE HAVE BEEN BEAT BY THE BEST TEAM THAT EVER PUT FOOT IN A FOOTBALL ENCLOSURE.*

AND, DAYS LATER, TO THE DELIGHT OF ALL, HAT-TRICK HERO FRED DEWHURST WAS OFFERED A PLACE IN THE CORINTHIANS TEAM! IT WAS WELL-DESERVED, AND A GREAT HONOUR, NOT JUST FOR FRED BUT FOR NORTH END, TOO.

AFTER CORINTHIANS, NORTH END DEFEATED FA CUP HOLDERS BLACKBURN ROVERS ON CHRISTMAS DAY, AND THEN EMBARKED ON AN UNBEATEN RUN THAT BECAME THE TALK OF FOOTBALL.

7 - 0!

NOTTS FOREST

9 - 1!

BURNLEY

7 - 0!

WEST BROM

4 - 1!

WOLVES

INVINCIBLE, A TELL THEE, INVINCIBLE!

HOWEVER, ALL GOOD THINGS MUST COME TO AN END - AND ON EASTER MONDAY, APRIL 1886, ACCRINGTON ACHIEVED THE IMPOSSIBLE...

YEESSS!

3 - 2!

...A SAID IT WUD 'APPEN!

AS THOUGH STILL IN SHOCK, NORTH END LOST AGAIN SHORTLY AFTERWARDS, TO WEST BROM, BUT IT MATTERED LITTLE - THEY HAD PLAYED 54 STRAIGHT GAMES WITHOUT DEFEAT, AND PRESTON NORTH END MARCHED INTO THE RECORD BOOKS!

AFTER THEIR INCREDIBLE SEASON - WINNING 59 OF 64 GAMES, AND SCORING 318 GOALS - NORTH END WERE THE MOST FAMOUS TEAM IN THE LAND.

THEY PLAY WITH MACHINE LIKE ACCURACY AND RIGID UNSELFISHNESS... THEY HAVE BROUGHT THE SHORT-PASSING GAME TO THE HIGHEST POINT OF PERFECTION EVER SEEN!

HUMPH, I SUPPOSE THEY DID BEAT THE VILLA.

IN PREPARATION FOR THE '86-87 CAMPAIGN, THEY WENT BACK ON THE ROAD - PLAYING 3 GAMES IN 3 DAYS ON A MINI TOUR OF SCOTLAND.

DUNDEE STRATHMORE	3 - 8 PNE
ARBROATH	2 - 6 PNE
THIRD LANARK	4 - 2 PNE

WITHIN A MONTH THEY RETURNED NORTH, TO PLAY THE MIGHTY QUEEN'S PARK IN GLASGOW - AND SCORED A FANTASTIC 6-1 WIN!

ALL EYES WERE NOW ON THE FA CUP. MOST OF SUDELL'S RECRUITS HAD BEEN RESIDENT FOR THE REQUIRED 2 YEARS, AND NORTH END AT LAST FELT READY TO BRING THE TROPHY TO DEEPDALE.

FA CUP, 1ST ROUND DRAW.

QUEEN'S PARK...

WILL PLAY...

PRESTON NORTH END.

FOR THE CUP, SUDELL HAD SIGNED A NEW GOALIE, AS BILLY ROSE WAS AS YET INELIGIBLE.

A CELEBRATED AMATEUR, ROSE HAD CAUSED A MAJOR STIR WHEN HE JOINED PRESTON'S ILLEGAL PROFESSIONALS IN MARCH 1885. AND TRUE TO FORM, SUDELL'S REPLACEMENT SIGNING WAS NO LESS CONTROVERSIAL. TAKE A BOW...

...ARTHUR WHARTON.

OOOOOH!

HAILING FROM JAMESTOWN ON AFRICA'S GOLDEN COAST, 21-YEAR-OLD WHARTON JOINED FROM DARLINGTON TO PLAY SOLELY IN FA CUP GAMES.

ALTHOUGH SIGNED AS AN 'AMATEUR', HE THUS BECAME THE FIRST BLACK MAN TO JOIN A PROFESSIONAL CLUB – WHICH RAISED EYEBROWS AMONGST VICTORIAN SOCIETY.

HOWEVER, SUDELL AND THE NORTH END WERE NOT TROUBLED BY RACIST OPINIONS, AND WERE ONLY TOO DELIGHTED TO HAVE SIGNED AN EXCEPTIONAL SPORTSMAN.

VIEWED AS AN UP-AND-COMING GOALKEEPER, WHARTON WAS ALSO A RENOWNED CYCLIST AND CRICKETER – AND HAD RECENTLY BEEN CROWNED AMATEUR ATHLETICS ASSOCIATION 100 YARDS CHAMPION!

HURRAAAAY!

CLOCKING A WORLD RECORD TIME OF 10 SECONDS!

ON THE PITCH HE WAS AN ECCENTRIC PERFORMER...

PLAY UP, GENTS!

AND PACKED A PUNCH!

THUMP!

OOOF!

AND HIS NORTH END DEBUT COULDN'T HAVE BEEN TOUGHER!

GLASGOW, SATURDAY 30TH OCTOBER, 1886.

NORTH END, WEARING WHITE, DEPARTED THE BEDFORD HOTEL TO FACE QUEEN'S PARK AT HAMPDEN.

AFTER A MORNING OF HEAVY SHOWERS, GLASGOW WAS BATHED IN SUNSHINE, AS 20,000 SPECTATORS TURNED OUT – ALL EAGER TO SEE THE SCOTTISH CUP HOLDERS AVENGE THEIR RECENT 6-1 LOSS!

BUT NORTH END HAD OTHER IDEAS, AS JACK GORDON...

1 - 0!

FRED DEWHURST...

2 - 0!

AND JIMMY ROSS...

3 - 0!

PUT THE GAME BEYOND REACH!

STILL SMARTING FROM THE LAST DEFEAT, THE CROWD WERE ALSO ANNOYED AT PNE'S SCOTTISH PLAYERS WHO'D LEFT TO PLAY IN ENGLAND.

TURNCOATS!

FLUKEY GOALS!

AND, JUST MINUTES FROM TIME...

AAAGGH!

A RECKLESS CHALLENGE FROM JIMMY ROSS ON HARROWER SENT THE ALREADY HOSTILE CROWD RAGING!

AND WHEN THE WHISTLE BLEW...

RUN!

STEADY, LADS!

GET 'IM!

HAVING GOT TO THE SAFETY OF THE PAVILION, JIMMY ROSS MADE HIS ESCAPE!

GOOD LUCK, JIM!

COME OOT, ROSS!

QUEEN'S PARK OFFICIALS GAVE HIM AN ULSTER COAT FOR A DISGUISE, AND THE POLICE FALSELY ANNOUNCED HE'D BEEN ARRESTED, TO CALM THE BAYING MOB!

HAVING BEATEN WITTON IN ROUND 2, PNE WENT BACK TO SCOTLAND TO PLAY RENTON IN ROUND 3 - DRAWING 3-3 AMIDST CONTROVERSIAL CIRCUMSTANCES AT TONTINE PARK. INCREDIBLY, A REPLAY WAS THEN ARRANGED AT HAMPDEN! THANKFULLY, A MUCH CALMER ATMOSPHERE ENSUED, AND NORTH END RAN OUT 2-0 WINNERS!

NO NEED TO CHECK *YOUR* BOOTS, GENTLEMEN. ON YOU GO!

GRANTED A BYE IN ROUND 4, PNE NEXT TRAVELLED SOUTH, TO EAST LONDON, TO FACE AMATEUR SIDE OLD FORESTERS. REFEREE FOR THE MATCH WAS CHARLES CRUMP, VICE-PRESIDENT OF THE FA, AND OLD ADVERSARY OF SUDELL FROM THE ROW OVER PROFESSIONALISM. BEFORE KICK-OFF, CRUMP MADE THE CUSTOMARY CHECK OF NORTH END'S BOOTS, BUT THEN...

IT WAS A BLATANT DISPLAY OF CRUMP'S CONTEMPT FOR THE WORKING-CLASS PROFESSIONALS. BUT IN THE END, SUDELL'S MEN HAD THE LAST LAUGH, AND WON COMFORTABLY, 3-0!

FOR THE 6TH ROUND JUST 4 DAYS LATER, NORTH END WERE DRAWN AWAY TO OLD CARTHUSIANS, WHICH MEANT ANOTHER LONG JOURNEY TO LONDON.

WEARY FROM THE DEMANDS OF TOO MUCH TRAVEL, THEY OFFERED OLD CARTHUSIANS £100 TO PLAY THE TIE AT DEEPDALE. BUT THIS WAS REFUSED, AND THE GAME KICKED-OFF AT KENNINGTON OVAL, ON WEDNESDAY 2ND MARCH, 1887.

IT WAS A BRUISING ENCOUNTER...

CARTHUSIANS ROUGHED UP NORTH END...

WHARTON MADE SOME GOOD BLOCKS...

AND BOB HOWARTH DEFENDED WELL...

AND WITH THE SCORE 1-1 AT FULL TIME...

GORDON'S SHOT SENT NORTH END THROUGH!

AFTER A HURRIED DINNER, PNE CAUGHT THE 8PM TRAIN TO PRESTON AND ARRIVED HOME AFTER 1AM. BY NOW THEY WERE THOROUGHLY EXHAUSTED.

SO FAR, THEY'D TRAVELLED 2,038 MILES TO PLAY THEIR CUP TIES!

WHEN THE SEMI-FINAL AGAINST WEST BROM WAS FIXED FOR 3 DAYS LATER, WILLIAM SUDELL ASKED THE FA IF THEY'D KINDLY RESCHEDULE - BUT THE PLEA WAS DECLINED.

COME THE 5TH MARCH, AND THE SEMI-FINAL WAS ALL TOO PREDICTABLE, AS A WORN-OUT PNE PROVED NO MATCH FOR A WELL-RESTED WEST BROM, AND ALTHOUGH SAM THOMSON SCORED FIRST, THE *THROSTLES* OVERPOWERED NORTH END – SCORING 2 IN THE LAST 10 MINUTES TO WIN 3-1.

THE UNDERDOGS HAD DEFEATED THE FAVOURITES, AND WEST BROM'S JOY WAS UNCONSTRAINED!

IN CONTRAST, THE 3,000 NORTH ENDERS WHO HAD ASSEMBLED ON FISHERGATE GREETED THE TELEGRAMMED NEWS WITH A DIGNIFIED, IF NOT DUMBFOUNDED, SILENCE.

THE FA CUP DREAM WAS OVER FOR ANOTHER YEAR, AND YET THERE WAS STILL A CHANCE OF SOME SILVERWARE...

FOLLOWING NORTH END'S APPARENT COLLAPSE, FELLOW FINALISTS BOLTON WANDERERS WERE QUICKLY INSTALLED AS FAVOURITES – BUT PNE NOW HAD 3 WEEKS IN WHICH TO REST. ALTHOUGH BEFORE THE FINAL, THEY DID HAVE JUST ONE MORE, RATHER IMPORTANT ENGAGEMENT TO ATTEND...

ON THE *12*TH MARCH, NORTH END RETURNED TO KENNINGTON OVAL, HONOURED WITH AN INVITATION TO PLAY A CHARITY MATCH AGAINST CORINTHIANS, AS PART OF QUEEN VICTORIA'S JUBILEE CELEBRATIONS.

CORINTHIANS WISHED TO SPORT THEIR WHITE JERSEYS, AND SO NORTH END WERE PROVIDED WITH NEW SHIRTS.

CLAP!

CLAP!

WILLIAM SUDELL AND CAPTAIN NICK ROSS WERE PRESENTED TO THE PRINCE OF WALES.

DURING THE GAME, THE PRINCE FAMOUSLY REMARKED UPON A NORTH END ATTACK...

I SAY! THAT MAN KICKED THE BALL WITH HIS HEAD!

FINAL SCORE: *1-1*

THE JUBILEE INVITATION ILLUSTRATED NORTH END'S ESTEEMED POSITION IN FOOTBALL, BUT ROYAL APPROVAL ALONE WASN'T ENOUGH. THE RECORD BOOKS POINTED TO AN EMPTY CABINET, AND IT WAS HIGH TIME SUDELL'S MEN PUT THAT RIGHT.

WINNING

We cannae play a cup-tie in this madness!

SAT. 26TH MARCH, 1887
LANCASHIRE CHALLENGE CUP
— FINAL TIE —
BOLTON WANDERERS
V.
PRESTON NORTH END

NORTH END:
W. ROSE
R. HOWARTH
N. ROSS (CAPT.)
D. RUSSELL
J. FERGUSON
J. GRAHAM
J. GORDON
J. ROSS
S. THOMSON
F. DEWHURST
G. DRUMMOND

OVER 15,000 DESCENDED ON BOLTON'S PIKES LANE GROUND, AS FANS CAME BY FOOT, CABS, WAGONS AND OMNIBUSES. SOME 3,000 NORTH ENDERS ARRIVED FROM PRESTON ON SPECIALLY RUN TRAINS.

BOLTON HAD DEFEATED NORTH END 3-0 THE PREVIOUS WEEK IN A FRIENDLY, AND THIS, ALONG WITH THE WHITES' COLLAPSE IN THE FA CUP, SAW THE WANDERERS PLACED AS FAVOURITES. BUT NOT EVERYONE AGREED...

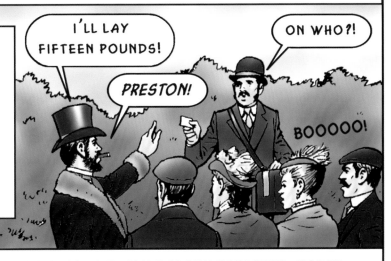

BOLTON WON THE TOSS...

AND NORTH END KICKED OFF AGAINST A STRONG WIND.

AFTER SOME EARLY BOLTON PRESSURE, NORTH END'S PASSING GAME CLICKED INTO GEAR...

DEWHURST STRUCK...

AND...

A-AAGH!

IT'S IN!

1-0!

JIMMY ROSS COULDN'T CONTAIN HIS DELIGHT!

GOOD MAN, FRED!

2 MINUTES LATER, FRED GOT ANOTHER!

2-0!

THEN, JUST BEFORE HALF-TIME...

JIMMY ROSS!

3-0!

THE SECOND HALF WAS MUCH MORE EVEN...

AARGH!

BUT WANDERERS COULDN'T BREAK THROUGH NORTH END'S STUBBORN DEFENCE.

AND THE MATCH ENDED 3-0!

PRESTON NORTH END WERE LANCASHIRE CHAMPIONS!

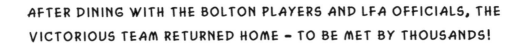

AFTER DINING WITH THE BOLTON PLAYERS AND LFA OFFICIALS, THE VICTORIOUS TEAM RETURNED HOME – TO BE MET BY THOUSANDS!

A BRASS BAND LED THE PARADE THROUGH TOWN, AS FIREWORKS WERE SET OFF AND THE CHAMPIONS OF LANCASHIRE CARRIED SHOULDER-HIGH TO THE FULWOOD CLUB!

DESPITE HEAVY RAIN, THE JUBILANT FOLK OF PRESTON TURNED OUT IN DROVES, TO SHOW SUDELL AND HIS TEAM JUST WHAT THEY MEANT TO THE TOWN.

HIP, HIP...

HURRAY!

A WEEK LATER, ON EASTER SATURDAY, THE TROPHY AND MEDALS WERE PRESENTED IN AN OFFICIAL CEREMONY AT THE PUBLIC HALL.

IN A WONDERFUL EVENING OF ENTERTAINMENT, HARRY YORKE GAVE A RENDITION OF *'THE MEN OF WHOM PRESTON MAY BE PROUD'*, BEFORE MR W. FORREST OF TURTON FC, AND VICE-PRESIDENT OF THE LANCASHIRE FOOTBALL ASSOCIATION, ADDRESSED THE CROWD...

I REMEMBER THE EARLY DAYS WHEN NORTH END, CAPTAINED BY MR SUDELL, VISITED TURTON, AND RECEIVED A TOWELLING! LATER, MR SUDELL TOLD ME HE'D MAKE NORTH END THE FINEST TEAM IN THE WORLD...

WELL, I CONGRATULATE YOU ON HAVING KEPT YOUR WORD!

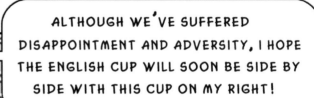

IT IS MY PLEASURE TO RECEIVE THIS TROPHY ON BEHALF OF THE NORTH END CLUB, AND, I MIGHT SAY, A GREAT NUMBER OF THE PEOPLE OF PRESTON.

ALTHOUGH WE'VE SUFFERED DISAPPOINTMENT AND ADVERSITY, I HOPE THE ENGLISH CUP WILL SOON BE SIDE BY SIDE WITH THIS CUP ON MY RIGHT!

HEAR HEAR!

FOR WE INTEND TO HAVE IT, COME WHAT MAY!

CLAP! CLAP!

BRAVO!

WHEN THE DUST HAD SETTLED ON THEIR SUCCESS, THE '87-88 SEASON BEGAN IN EARNEST, AND BROUGHT WITH IT A CHANGE BETWEEN THE STICKS.

JAMES TRAINER

ARTHUR WHARTON AND BILLY ROSE HAD LEFT, AND A REPLACEMENT ARRIVED FROM BOLTON WANDERERS IN THE SHAPE OF WELSH CUSTODIAN JAMES TRAINER.

TRAINER WAS INELIGIBLE FOR FA CUP GAMES, THANKS TO THE PESKY RESIDENTIAL CLAUSE, SO FOR THEIR 1ST ROUND TIE AT HOME TO THE MINNOWS OF HYDE FC, NORTH END TURNED TO FRED ADDISON – THEIR RELATIVELY INEXPERIENCED RESERVE TEAM KEEPER, WHO STOOD 5 FT 1 INCH TALL.

SCOTTISH CLUBS HAD NOW WITHDRAWN FROM THE ENGLISH FA CUP, AND, DUE TO NORTH END'S EXTREME TRAVELLING OF THE PREVIOUS SEASON, THE FA HAD DECIDED THE FIRST THREE ROUNDS BE REGIONAL AFFAIRS.

15TH OCTOBER, 1887. PNE v HYDE.

ONLY 2,000 SPECTATORS TURNED OUT TO WATCH A GAME, THAT ALL AGREED WAS A MISMATCH. HOWEVER, THOSE WHO DID WERE TO WITNESS HISTORY BEING MADE.

I HEAR THE ENGLISH RECORD IS IN DANGER TODAY!

EH? MORE THAN 19-0?

NO CHANCE!

WORD HAD SPREAD THAT NORTH END WOULD BE TRYING FOR SOMETHING SPECIAL, AND MANY BETS HAD BEEN PLACED.

SUDELL'S MEN WERE ON A MISSION, AND AFTER JUST 3 MINUTES...

1-0!

DEWHURST!

SOON AFTER, THOMSON HIT A ROCKET...

OOOOH!

AND DRUMMOND RUSHED IN...

2-0!

AND THE GOALS KEPT ON COMING...

SIX!

EIGHT!

TEN!

BY HALF-TIME, IT WAS 12-0!

HARD LUCK, SON.

AFTER NORTH END'S THIRD GOAL, HYDE'S CENTRE-BACK, BOWERS, HAD RETIRED WITH A SPRAINED ARM. BUT AT THE START OF THE SECOND HALF, PNE (AGAINST THE RULES) SPORTINGLY ALLOWED HYDE TO FIELD A REPLACEMENT PLAYER.

COULD THIS HAVE BEEN THE FIRST EVER SUBSTITUTION IN THE FA CUP — ALBEIT ILLEGAL?!

THE SECOND HALF CONTINUED WHERE THE FIRST HAD LEFT OFF, AND WITH ALMOST THE LAST KICK OF THE GAME, JOHN GOODALL SCORED HIS FIRST...

TWENTY-SIX!

FINAL SCORE: 26-0. GOALS: J. ROSS 7, THOMSON 5, GORDON 5, DEWHURST 3, DRUMMOND 2, GRAHAM 1, N. ROSS 1, RUSSELL 1, GOODALL 1.

THERE WAS NO SHAME FOR HYDE'S GOALKEEPER, CHARLES BUNYAN, WHOSE HEROICS WERE CHEERED BY ALL.

IN FUTURE YEARS, BUNYAN MOVED INTO MANAGEMENT AND COACHED THE FAMOUS BELGIAN CLUB, ANDERLECHT, AS WELL AS SWEDEN'S 1912 OLYMPIC TEAM!

AS FOR PRESTON NORTH END, THEY'D GONE FOR THE RECORD — AND SMASHED IT.

THOSE BITTER DISAPPOINTMENTS OF THE PAST HAD FORGED A COLD, RUTHLESS STREAK. NORTH END MEANT BUSINESS — AND THEY WANTED EVERYONE TO KNOW.

AFTER WINS VERSUS EVERTON (6-0) AND HALLIWELL (4-0), PRESTON WERE GRANTED A BYE IN THE 4TH ROUND. BUT WHEN BOLTON PROTESTED THEIR 1ST ROUND VICTORS, EVERTON, HAD FIELDED INELIGIBLE PLAYERS, NORTH END WERE OBLIGED TO ENTERTAIN A REINSTATED WANDERERS AT DEEPDALE.

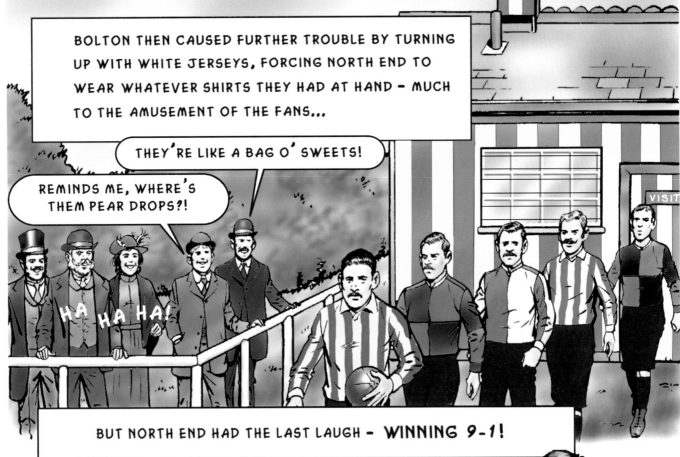

BOLTON THEN CAUSED FURTHER TROUBLE BY TURNING UP WITH WHITE JERSEYS, FORCING NORTH END TO WEAR WHATEVER SHIRTS THEY HAD AT HAND — MUCH TO THE AMUSEMENT OF THE FANS...

THEY'RE LIKE A BAG O' SWEETS!

REMINDS ME, WHERE'S THEM PEAR DROPS?!

HA HA HA!

BUT NORTH END HAD THE LAST LAUGH — **WINNING 9-1!**

STILL IN NEED OF A CUP-TIE KEEPER, SUDELL PULLED YET ANOTHER MASTERSTROKE AND SIGNED, DR ROBERT HERBERT MILLS-ROBERTS OF CORINTHIANS. JUST LIKE ARTHUR WHARTON BEFORE HIM, MILLS-ROBERTS SIGNED PURELY AS AN AMATEUR, AND WOULD CONDUCT HIS TIME BETWEEN FA CUP GAMES AND HIS DAY JOB, AS HOUSE SURGEON AT BIRMINGHAM GENERAL HOSPITAL.

DR MILLS-ROBERTS

ANOTHER ADDITION TO THE FIRST TEAM SQUAD WAS LOCAL LAD ROBERT 'BOB' HOLMES, WHO WAS PROMOTED FROM THE RESERVES. A FULL-BACK OF SOME MERIT, 19-YEAR-OLD BOB ACTUALLY WORKED A FULL 24-HOUR STRETCH ON THE RAILWAY BEFORE MAKING ONLY HIS SECOND START FOR THE SENIOR TEAM!

BOB HOLMES

THE FA CUP'S 5TH ROUND GRIPPED THE WHOLE OF FOOTBALL, AS FAVOURITES NORTH END WERE DRAWN AWAY TO THE HOLDERS, ASTON VILLA.

NORTH END HAD A PREARRANGED FIXTURE FOR THE GIVEN DATE AND APPEALED TO HAVE THE TIE PUT BACK, WHICH 'COINCIDENTALLY', WOULD ALLOW DR MILLS-ROBERTS TO PLAY, AS HIS REGISTRATION WAS NOT YET COMPLETE. REALISING THIS, VILLA DECLINED TO SUPPORT THE APPEAL, AND THE FA REFUSED IT, FURTHER FUELLING THE ANTAGONISM PRESTON FANS FELT TOWARDS THE ASSOCIATION.

TO PREPARE, SUDELL SENT HIS TEAM TO THE PALACE HOTEL – A HYDROPATHIC ESTABLISHMENT IN SOUTHPORT, WHERE THEY UNDERWENT A WEEK-LONG TRAINING REGIME UNDER THE CHARGE OF FAMOUS ATHLETE J. CONCANNON.

EARLY STARTS...

GERR-UUUUP!

ICE-COLD, SALTWATER PLUNGE BATHS...

AOOOWHH-F-F-F-FFF!

BRISK WALKS...

LOOK SHARP, BOYS!

AND LOTS AND LOTS OF PRACTICE...

AM BEAT!

QUICKER, LADS, QUICKER!

CONCANNON'S COMMANDS WERE CARRIED OUT TO THE LETTER. IT WAS DECLARED THE TEAM HAD NEVER BEEN IN BETTER SHAPE!

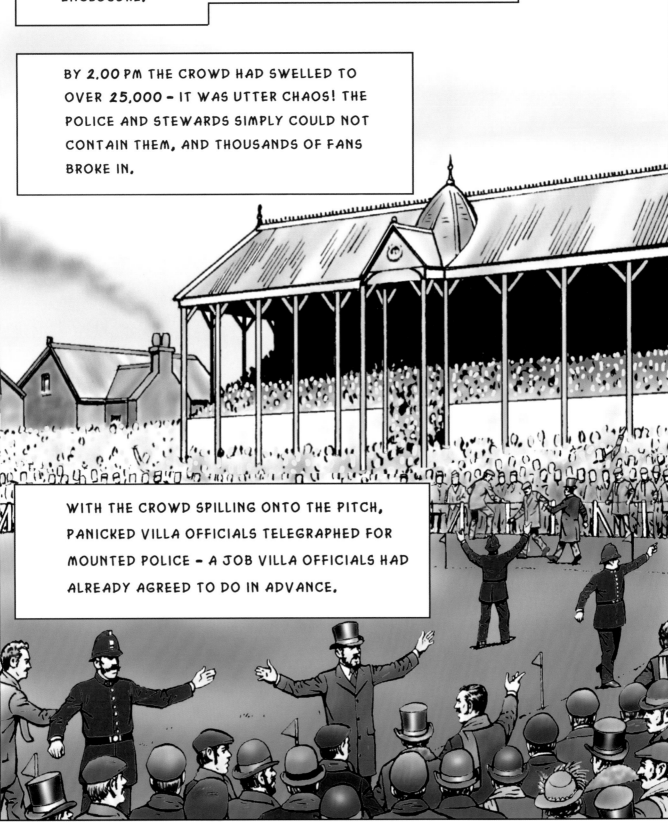

SATURDAY 7TH JANUARY, 1888.
ASTON VILLA v. PRESTON NORTH END.

IT WAS A FINE DAY. THE GATES OPENED AT 12.00 PM, AND BY 1.30 PM OVER 12,000 HAD ENTERED THE PERRY BARR ENCLOSURE.

BY 2.00 PM THE CROWD HAD SWELLED TO OVER 25,000 – IT WAS UTTER CHAOS! THE POLICE AND STEWARDS SIMPLY COULD NOT CONTAIN THEM, AND THOUSANDS OF FANS BROKE IN.

WITH THE CROWD SPILLING ONTO THE PITCH, PANICKED VILLA OFFICIALS TELEGRAPHED FOR MOUNTED POLICE – A JOB VILLA OFFICIALS HAD ALREADY AGREED TO DO IN ADVANCE.

SOMEHOW THE GAME BEGAN. BUT JUST A FEW MINUTES IN...

LOOK OUT!

A-AAGHH!

WHEN PLAY RESTARTED, SOME 13 MINUTES LATER, THE HOME SIDE RUSHED AT NORTH END'S GOAL...

GET IN, ARCHIE!

AND CAPTAIN ARCHIE HUNTER PUT THE VILLANS ONE UP!

NORTH END REPLIED, AND GOODALL WENT CLOSE...

OOOOH!

THWACK!

THEN, WHEN A VILLA GOAL WAS RULED OUT FOR OFFSIDE, HUNDREDS COLLAPSED ONTO THE FIELD ONCE MORE.

WE CANNAE PLAY A CUP-TIE IN THIS MADNESS!

WITH ALL THE STOPPAGES, NICK ROSS PLEADED FOR THE MATCH TO BE CHANGED TO A FRIENDLY. BUT, PERHAPS SENSING VICTORY, VILLA'S CAPTAIN DECLINED TO SUPPORT HIM.

THANKFULLY, 3 OFF-DUTY HUSSARS IN UNDRESS UNIFORM MANAGED TO ACQUIRE SOME CAB HORSES AND HELPED TO FORCE THE CROWD BACK!

THE FOOTBALL WORLD HAD NEVER SEEN THE LIKE!

WHEN PLAY RESTARTED, A FIRED-UP NICK ROSS WOWED THE CROWD.

THAS HALF THE FIELD!

GRADUALLY NORTH END TOOK CONTROL, AND JUST BEFORE HALF-TIME...

DEWHURST!

1 - 1!

THE FIRST HALF HAD TAKEN NO LESS THAN 80 MINUTES!

IN THE SECOND HALF, A TIRED VILLA ADOPTED NEW TACTICS...

AAAAOWGH!

BOOO!

BOOO!

FAIRATION, REF!

BUT PNE KEPT THEIR COOL, AND AFTER SOME GREAT COMBINATION PLAY...

THE LITTLE DEMON!

JIMMY ROSS!

ASTON VILLA 1.
NORTH END 2.

THEN, WITH 20 MINUTES LEFT...

GO ON, JIMMY!

THE 'LITTLE DEMON' TURNED PROVIDER...

JOHNNY GOODALL!

ASTON VILLA 1.
NORTH END 3.

JUST BEFORE FULL-TIME THE ARMY OF MOUNTED POLICE ARRIVED TO PREVENT A POSSIBLE INVASION!

THE EPIC CONTEST WAS FINALLY OVER... OR WAS IT?

RESULT IN DOUBT - PROTEST.

The game was played under protest, on account of the spectators breaking

VILLA PROTESTED THAT THE TIE SHOULD BE REPLAYED - CLAIMING THE REFEREE AND BOTH CAPTAINS HAD AGREED THAT THE GAME BE CHANGED TO A FRIENDLY, DUE TO THE CONSTANT INCURSIONS OF THE CROWD!

BOTH UMPIRES, J.E. CLEGG AND C. HUGHES, BACKED UP THIS CLAIM!

BOTH CAPTAINS MUST AGREE!

BUT REFEREE M. P. BETTS REFUTED THE CLAIM, AND REPORTED THAT VILLA'S CAPTAIN HAD FAILED TO SUPPORT NICK ROSS, AND THAT NO AGREEMENT HAD TAKEN PLACE.

INCENSED BY THE PROTEST, A FURIOUS WILLAIM SUDELL THREATENED TO WITHDRAW NORTH END FROM THE COMPETITION IF THE TIE MUST BE REPLAYED – MUCH TO THE CONSTERNATION OF THE CLUB AND ITS SUPPORTERS!

THANKFULLY, TO THE RELIEF OF ALL NORTH ENDERS, THE FA TOOK BETTS' REPORT AS FINAL. NORTH END MARCHED INTO THE NEXT ROUND AND CONTINUED DOING WHAT THEY DID BEST...

WINNING...

NORTH END VICTORIOUS

WINNING...

INVINCIBLES WIN AGAIN!

AND WINNING.

ANOTHER FIVE-NIL!

AYE, 'TIS GETTIN' BORIN' NOW!

BY THE 10TH MARCH 1888, THEY'D SET A PHENOMENAL RECORD:

42 CONSECUTIVE GAMES WON
241 GOALS SCORED
46 CONCEDED
...INVINCIBLE?

WHAT'S MORE, AFTER DEFEATING SHEFFIELD WEDNESDAY AND CREWE ALEXANDRA, NORTH END HAD REACHED **THEIR FIRST FA CUP FINAL!** THE DREAM WAS CLOSE, AND ONLY ONE TEAM STOOD IN THEIR WAY – WEST BROMWICH ALBION.

FOUNDERS

MAKE SURE THEY DON'T GET PAID!

BEATEN FINALISTS THE PREVIOUS TWO YEARS, WEST BROM STARTED WELL.

MILLS-ROBERTS STOPPED A VICIOUS STRIKE...

YOUNG STARLET BILLY BASSETT SEIZED THE REBOUND...

TRICKED GRAHAM...

MILLS-ROBERTS RUSHED OUT...

AND LEFT BAYLISS A FREE SHOT!

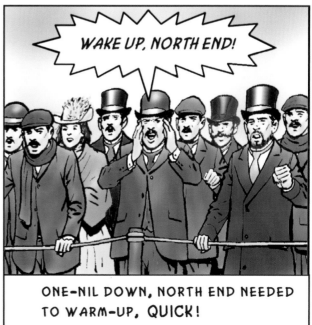

ONE-NIL DOWN, NORTH END NEEDED TO WARM-UP, QUICK!

THE GOAL STUNNED NORTH END INTO LIFE, BUT BOB ROBERTS IN THE WEST BROM GOAL WAS IN DETERMINED FORM...

OHH, WHAT A STOP!

AND AGAIN!

IN THE SECOND HALF NORTH END CONTINUED PRESSING, UNTIL FINALLY...

GET IT, FRED!

A-UGHFF!

YEESSS!

...THE PRESSURE PAID OFF!

NEWS OF DEWHURST'S GOAL WAS TELEGRAMMED AND POSTED ON THE WINDOWS OF *THE LANCASHIRE EVENING POST'S* OFFICES ON FISHERGATE...

HURRAH!

HURRAH!

WE'LL TAKE THE POT NOW!

ALL EXPECTED NORTH END TO GO ON AND WIN!

BUT THEN, JUST 10 MINUTES FROM TIME...

WOODHALL STRUCK...

IT'S...

AND...

...IN!

PRESTONIAN HEARTS WERE BROKEN.

SUDELL'S MEN RALLIED BUT COULDN'T REPLY AND WEST BROM WON THE FA CUP 2-1. IT WAS NORTH END'S FIRST DEFEAT SINCE THE 18TH AUGUST 1887, AND LATER WEST BROM'S BILLY BASSETT WOULD REMARK:

WE BEAT THEM, BUT I DON'T PRETEND FOR A MOMENT WE DESERVED TO BEAT THEM.

BACK HOME, *THE PRESTON CHRONICLE* SUMMED UP THE MOOD OF THE FISHERGATE CROWD:

The whole multitude were stunned - heads down, crests fallen, faces despondant, hands in pockets, and a slow, silent movement out of the street, as if the bulk of the crowd had been sentenced to be gibbetted or hanged, without any hope of mercy.

THEN ADDED, RATHER UNKINDLY:

Served them right - for being such fools as to think that the North Enders were an absolute perfect body, and quite out of reach of defeat.

MANY WHO SAW THE FINAL DECLARED NORTH END UNLUCKY AND QUESTIONED THE DECISIONS OF REFEREE MAJOR MARINDIN - THE OLD FOE OF WILLIAM SUDELL. INDEED, CAMBRIDGE UNIVERSITY'S CAPTAIN, TINSLEY LINDLEY, LATER COMMENTED TO NICK ROSS...

YOU CANNOT EXPECT TO WIN WHEN PLAYING AGAINST ELEVEN PLAYERS AND THE DEVIL!

YET SUDELL, WHO HAD THREATENED TO RETIRE SHOULD NORTH END BE VICTORIOUS, WAS TYPICALLY DIGNIFIED AND RESOLUTE.

A MAN WHO CANNOT LOSE IS NOT FIT TO WIN.

I SHALL HAVE ANOTHER TRY, AND IF I AM KNOCKED DOWN NEXT YEAR, I WILL TRY AGAIN AND AGAIN.

IT WILL BE OUR TURN TO WIN IT SOME DAY!

HOWEVER, NOT ALL SHARED SUDELL'S UNSHAKEABLE BELIEF, AND WHEN TEAM CAPTAIN AND TALISMAN NICK ROSS LEFT TO JOIN EVERTON AFTER A FALL-OUT WITH SUDELL, THE VULTUROUS DOOM-MONGERS SET TO WORK...

GETTIN' ON NOW, MISSED THEIR CHANCE!

WE'LL STRUGGLE WITHOUT NICK ROSS!

MARK MY WORDS - GOLDEN AGE IS OVER!

IN THE FIVE YEARS SINCE THE SUMMER OF '83, NORTH END HAD WON 241 GAMES, LOST ONLY 26, AND SCORED OVER 1,300 GOALS. IT WAS A FANTASTIC ACHIEVEMENT. BUT FOR ALL THEIR FAME AND RECORDS, THE FA CUP CONTINUED TO ELUDE THEM. PEOPLE STARTED TO MOCK SUDELL AND HIS QUEST FOR THE TROPHY. EVEN AFTER SUCH A REMARKABLE SEASON, THEY CLAIMED HIS TEAM WERE FINISHED. YET THOSE WHO BELIEVED THIS WERE STRONGLY MISTAKEN, FOR THE TRUTH WAS FAR FROM IT - PRESTON NORTH END WERE ONLY WARMING UP.

THREE WEEKS BEFORE THE FA CUP FINAL, ON THE 2ND MARCH, A LETTER ARRIVED AT FIVE OF THE LEADING CLUBS IN ENGLAND: ASTON VILLA, BLACKBURN ROVERS, BOLTON WANDERERS, PRESTON NORTH END, AND WEST BROMWICH ALBION.

Every year it is becoming more and more difficult for football clubs of any standing to meet their friendly arrangements and even arrange friendly matches. The consequence is that at the last moment, through cup-tie interference, clubs are compelled to take on teams who will not attract the public.

I beg to tender the following suggestion as a means of getting over the difficulty: that ten or twelve of the most prominent clubs in England combine to arrange home-and-away fixtures to be arranged at a friendly conference about the same time as the international conference.

The combination might be known as the 'Association Football Union'; even the suggested matches might be played under cup-tie rules, however, this is a detail.

THE LETTER WAS WRITTEN BY **41** YEAR OLD WILLIAM McGREGOR, A DRAPER FROM BRACO IN PERTHSHIRE, WHO HAD MOVED SOUTH TO BIRMINGHAM IN **1870** AND OPENED A LINEN DRAPERY SHOP IN ASTON.

BY **1888** HE WAS A SUCCESSFUL BUSINESSMAN AND A HUGELY INFLUENTIAL FIGURE AT ASTON VILLA, WHERE HE WAS ON THE BOARD OF DIRECTORS AND INVOLVED IN FOOTBALL AT ALL LEVELS.

McGREGOR HAD ALSO BEEN A STRONG SUPPORTER OF THE PUSH FOR PROFESSIONALISM – A RARITY IN THE MIDLANDS AT THE TIME.

THE PROPOSAL SPARKED GREAT INTEREST, AND A MEETING TOOK PLACE ON THE EVE OF THE FA CUP FINAL AT ANDERTON'S HOTEL IN LONDON. NORTH END DID NOT ATTEND.

MCGREGOR'S IDEA WAS INSPIRED BY THE COUNTY CRICKET CHAMPIONSHIP FORMAT AND FUELLED BY THE FINANCIAL WANTS OF THE PROFESSIONAL CLUBS, WHOSE EVER-RISING WAGE BILLS DEMANDED GOOD ATTENDANCE LEVELS TO KEEP THE BOOKS BALANCED.

UNSURPRISINGLY, RESISTANCE CAME FROM THE SOUTH, WHERE MOST CLUBS STILL ADHERED TO THE AMATEUR IDEAL. BUT THERE'D LONG BEEN TALK OF AN ALTERNATIVE TO THE FA CUP, AND THE MOVEMENT GATHERED STRENGTH WITH A SECOND MEETING ARRANGED FOR TUESDAY 17TH APRIL AT THE ROYAL HOTEL IN MANCHESTER. THIS TIME, NORTH END DID ATTEND.

12 CLUBS WERE CHOSEN AND, CONTROVERSIALLY, NOT EVERY TEAM THAT WAS PUT FORWARD MADE THE CUT. IT WAS SUGGESTED SOME WERE ADMITTED PURELY ON THEIR ABILITY TO DRAW LARGE CROWDS!

AS FOR THE NAME...

MAY I SUGGEST: THE FOOTBALL LEAGUE.

I PROPOSE: THE ASSOCIATION FOOTBALL UNION.

SUDELL'S PROPOSAL WAS ACCEPTED, AND HE WAS ALSO HONOURED WITH THE POSITION OF THE LEAGUE'S FIRST TREASURER. AS FOR MCGREGOR, HE WAS RIGHTLY ELECTED CHAIRMAN, AND IS FOREVER REMEMBERED WITH FONDNESS AS THE FATHER OF THE FOOTBALL LEAGUE.

THE FOOTBALL LEAGUE FOUNDED 1888

ACCRINGTON

ASTON VILLA

BLACKBURN ROVERS

BOLTON WANDERERS

BURNLEY

DERBY COUNTY

EVERTON

NOTTS COUNTY

PRESTON NORTH END

STOKE CITY

WEST BROMWICH ALBION

WOLVERHAMPTON WANDERERS

DEEPDALE, SATURDAY 8TH SEPTEMBER, 1888 - THE OPENING DAY OF THE FOOTBALL LEAGUE.

'TIS A NEW DAWN, GENTLEMEN - A FRESH CHALLENGE.

LET'S SILENCE THE DOUBTERS AND WIN THIS LEAGUE!

WE ARE THE NORTH END - AND TO BE THE FIRST CHAMPIONS IS A THING WORTH FIGHTING FOR!

ONE OTHER THING...

YOU ALL KNOW BURNLEY HAVE PUT IN EXTRA PRACTICE - AND ARE PROMISED A BONUS OF TEN SHILLINGS EACH TO WIN TODAY...

MAKE SURE THEY DON'T GET PAID!

ON A SUNNY AUTUMN AFTERNOON, FULLY 6,000 SPECTATORS ATTENDED DEEPDALE TO WATCH NORTH END PLAY BURNLEY.

NORTH END:
TRAINER
HOWARTH
HOLMES
W. GRAHAM
ROBERTSON
J. GRAHAM
GORDON
ROSS
GOODALL
DEWHURST
DRUMMOND

THE VISITORS ARRIVED LATE, AND IT WAS 3.50 PM BEFORE THE MATCH COULD START. WHEN IT DID, NORTH END ATTACKED FROM THE OFF – AND DEWHURST SHOT WIDE AFTER A MAZY DRIBBLE!

BURNLEY CAME BACK WITH A SHOT FROM YATES...

BUT HOLMES BLOCKED, AND SENT NORTH END RACING DOWNFIELD...

THAS IT, BOB!

GOODALL PICKED IT UP, AND PLAYED IT THROUGH TO ROSS...

JIM!

WHO IN TURN FED DEWHURST...

FRED!

AND...

GOAL!

FRED DEWHURST SCORED NORTH END'S FIRST EVER LEAGUE GOAL, AFTER JUST 2 MINUTES!

ONE MINUTE LATER...

WHAT A START!

2-0!

CLAP!

CLAP!

JACK GORDON ADDED A SECOND WITH A SUPERB STRIKE HIGH INTO THE GOAL!

IN THE END, ALTHOUGH BURNLEY PUT UP A SPIRITED FIGHT, THEY COULDN'T STOP THE DEEPDALIANS, WHO RAN OUT 5-2 WINNERS THANKS TO ANOTHER GOAL FROM DEWHURST AND TWO FROM JIMMY ROSS!

PRESTON NORTH END AND THE FOOTBALL LEAGUE WERE UP AND RUNNING!

INVINCIBLE

*...cloaked in mist
and glory...*

FIVE STRAIGHT VICTORIES FOLLOWED THE BURNLEY GAME, WITH NOTABLE HOME WINS VERSUS WOLVES (4-0) AND WEST BROM (3-0), AND A 7-0 DRUBBING OF STOKE - IN WHICH JIMMY ROSS GRABBED FOUR! INDEED, JAMES TRAINER, ELIGIBLE TO PLAY LEAGUE GAMES, OFTEN HAD LITTLE TO DO...

LEND US YOUR BROLLY, JIM!

HA HA HAA!

STOP 'IM!

BUT IT WASN'T ALL PLAIN SAILING. AWAY AT DERBY COUNTY THEY HAD TO FIGHT FROM TWO GOALS DOWN TO WIN 3-2, AND AT ACCRINGTON ON THE 20TH OCTOBER, GEORGE HAWORTH RAN THE WHITES RAGGED, AS JAMES TRAINER SHOWED WHY HE WOULD LATER BE CALLED 'THE PRINCE OF GOALKEEPERS' AND HELPED HIS TEAM CLING ON FOR A 0-0 DRAW!

SUCH WAS THEIR LEVEL OF PERFORMANCE OVER THE YEARS, THAT ANY DIP IN FORM WAS MAGNIFIED, THEN CRITICISED. THEY'D RODE THEIR LUCK AGAINST ACCRINGTON AND ADDED WEIGHT TO TO THE OPINION THAT THEY WERE ON THE WANE. AND DESPITE IMPRESSIVE WINS IN THE NEXT TWO GAMES, THE KNIVES CAME OUT AGAIN WHEN ASTON VILLA SNATCHED A 1-1 DRAW AT DEEPDALE.

'ARK AT THIS, LUV! SAYS THEY WERE A DISGRACE!

A DISGRACE!

BOB!

BUT SUDELL'S MEN WERE A RESILIENT BUNCH, AND IF ANYTHING THEY WERE ACTUALLY IMPROVING! TRAINER WAS SOLID IN GOAL, AND IN FRONT OF HIM BOB HOLMES HAD REVERTED TO HIS NATURAL POSITION AND FILLED THE SLOT VACATED BY NICK ROSS, TO FORM A STRONG BACK-LINE ALONGSIDE FELLOW PRESTONIAN BOB HOWARTH.

THEIR FORWARDS WERE SKILFUL AND PROLIFIC, AND PLAYERS LIKE DAVIE RUSSELL AND JACK GRAHAM PROVIDED STEEL IN THE MIDDLE OF THE PARK. AS A GROUP THEY WERE A FINELY TUNED PASSING MACHINE AND POSSESSED A NEVER-SAY-DIE SPIRIT, LONG INSTILLED BY SUDELL AND THE TENACIOUS NICK ROSS.

COME THE NEW YEAR, NORTH END REMAINED UNBEATEN AND STOOD ATOP THE LEAGUE. IN NOVEMBER A POINTS SYSTEM HAD BEEN PUT IN PLACE: 2 FOR A WIN, 1 FOR A DRAW, AND WITH 4 GAMES LEFT TO PLAY, IF THE WHITES WON THEIR NEXT MATCH AT HOME TO NOTTS COUNTY, AND SECOND-PLACED VILLA SLIPPED UP AT BURNLEY, THE DEEPDALIANS WOULD CLAIM THE TITLE!

DEEPDALE, SATURDAY 5TH JANUARY, 1889. PRESTON NORTH END v. NOTTS COUNTY.

NORTH END HAD AN EARLY GOAL DISALLOWED BUT CONTINUED TO PRESS, AND SURE ENOUGH...

1-0!

GOODALL!

JACK EDWARDS ADDED ANOTHER, AND NORTH END LED 2-0 AT THE BREAK. ALL LOOKED WELL, BUT...

...MINUTES INTO THE SECOND HALF, A FOG SETTLED OVER DEEPDALE, SO DENSE THAT NOBODY IN THE 4,000-STRONG CROWD HAD A CLEAR VIEW OF THE FIELD!

BUT THE GAME CONTINUED APACE, AND THOUGH COUNTY PULLED ONE BACK, FIRST EDWARDS AND THEN GOODALL...

4 - 1!

ARGH!

...SCORED ONE MORE EACH, TO MAKE THE GAME SAFE!

MEANWHILE, AT BURNLEY...

THERE'S ANOTHER!

BURNLEY 4.
ASTON VILLA 0.

BACK AT DEEPDALE...

PPHWEEEPPP!!!

THAS IT!

IS IT?!

IT WAS.

ON THEIR HOME TURF STOOD PRESTON NORTH END, CLOAKED IN MIST AND GLORY - PROUD CHAMPIONS OF THE FIRST EVER FOOTBALL LEAGUE!

THEY'D ACHIEVED IT WITH 3 GAMES TO SPARE, AND NOW ONE QUESTION REMAINED- COULD THEY UNDERLINE THEIR SUPREMACY AND FINISH UNDEFEATED?

THE RECORD ALMOST WENT IN THE VERY NEXT GAME, AT BLACKBURN! BUT A LATE ROVERS GOAL WAS DISALLOWED, TO SAVE A 2-2 DRAW! THEN A 2-0 WIN AT EVERTON LEFT A FINAL SHOWDOWN AWAY TO SECOND-PLACE ASTON VILLA, WHO FANCIED THEIR CHANCES HAVING DRAWN AT DEEPDALE. IT COULDN'T HAVE BEEN SCRIPTED BETTER!

BIRMINGHAM, SATURDAY 9TH FEB, 1889. THINGS DIDN'T START TOO WELL...

DUE TO A DELAY, PNE ARRIVED IN BIRMINGHAM ONLY MINUTES BEFORE KICK-OFF. HAVING ALREADY CHANGED ON THE TRAIN, THEY JUMPED ON AN OPEN WAGONETTE IN A MAD DASH TO THE PERRY BARR GROUND!

THERE WAS NO TIME FOR A TEAM TALK OR A WARM-UP. AND YET, DESPITE THEIR PANICKED START, NORTH END WENT ON TO PRODUCE ONE OF THEIR FINEST EVER DISPLAYS, *AND WON 2-0!* FRED DEWHURST SCORED BOTH AS THE WHITES' PRECISION PASSING PROVED TOO MUCH FOR THE VILLANS!

THE *DAILY STAR* REPORTED:

Villa fancied themselves able of victory after their draw at Deepdale, but North End, in the second half especially, put in a performance of such magnitude, that they completely outclassed the second place team on their own ground.

THE FOOTBALL LEAGUE, 1888-89.

		P	W	D	L	F	A	PTS
1	PRESTON NORTH END	22	18	4	0	74	15	40
2	ASTON VILLA	22	12	5	5	61	43	29
3	WOLVERHAMPTON WANDERERS	22	12	4	6	50	37	28
4	BLACKBURN ROVERS	22	10	6	6	66	45	26
5	BOLTON WANDERERS	22	10	2	10	63	59	22
6	WEST BROMWICH ALBION	22	10	2	10	40	46	22
7	ACCRINGTON	22	6	8	8	48	48	20
8	EVERTON	22	9	2	11	35	46	20
9	BURNLEY	22	7	3	12	42	62	17
10	DERBY COUNTY	22	7	2	13	41	60	16
11	NOTTS COUNTY	22	5	2	15	39	73	12
12	STOKE	22	4	4	14	26	51	12

THE PLAUDITS WERE MANY. NORTH END'S OUTSTANDING ACHIEVEMENT HAD SILENCED THE DOUBTERS AND HELPED ELEVATE THE LEAGUE IN THE PUBLIC'S IMAGINATION. NOW THE PUBLIC BEGAN TO TALK OF AN UNPRECEDENTED DOUBLE. COULD THE *INVINCIBLES* OF DEEPDALE FINALLY BE ON COURSE TO BREAK THEIR HOODOO AND CLAIM FOOTBALL'S MOST COVETED PRIZE?!

PNE HAD ALREADY WON THEIR OPENING FA CUP TIE, 3-0 AT BOOTLE, BUT IN DOING SO LOST SANDY ROBERTSON WITH A BROKEN COLLARBONE...

THANKFULLY, Dr MILLS-ROBERTS WAS ON HAND TO HELP AFTERWARDS.

THE 2ND ROUND BROUGHT HARSH CONDITIONS AND A TOUGH FIXTURE AWAY TO GRIMSBY TOWN...

AOOOF!

BUT GOALS FROM ROSS AND GOODALL SAW NORTH END THROUGH, 2-0!

THE 3RD ROUND BROUGHT BIRMINGHAM ST. GEORGE TO DEEPDALE, *AND ANOTHER 2-0 WIN!* A RARE GOAL FROM BOB HOLMES AND ONE FROM SAM THOMSON SAW THE WHITES DEFEAT THE DRAGONS TO MOVE INTO THE SEMI-FINALS! AND WHO AWAITED THEM...?

FLAMIN' WEST BROM... AGAIN!

HELD AT SHEFFIELD'S FAMOUS BRAMALL LANE GROUND, THE SEMI-FINAL DREW HUGE INTEREST. AN ESTIMATED 22,000 FANS PAID IN ON THE DAY, AND THOUSANDS MORE BROKE IN! EVERY AVAILABLE SPACE WAS OCCUPIED, WITH FANS SITTING ON TOP OF THE LARGE COVERED STAND AND THE ROOFS OF NEARBY HOUSES! THE CRAMMED-IN SPECTATORS ENCROACHED RIGHT ONTO THE TOUCHLINES AND PREDICTABLY, JUST MINUTES IN, THEY SPILLED OVER ONTO THE FIELD AND THE MATCH WAS STOPPED.

FORTUNATELY THE POLICE, AIDED BY THE MAYOR OF SHEFFIELD HIMSELF, MANAGED TO FORCE THE CROWD BACK...

BACK THEE GO, SONNY!

ALBEIT UNCEREMONIOUSLY!

AS FOR THE GAME, NORTH END DOMINATED AND *WON 1-0,* WITH A 35TH MINUTE GOAL BY DAVIE RUSSELL!

IT SHOULD'VE BEEN MORE, BUT NO PRESTONIAN CARED. THE WEST BROM JINX WAS BURIED – *AND PNE WERE BACK IN THE FINAL!*

WOLVERHAMPTON WANDERERS AWAITED IN THE FINAL. SINCE THE WHITES HAD ALREADY SCORED 2 CONVINCING WINS AGAINST THE WOLVES, THE EARNEST FOLK OF PRESTON SUCCUMBED TO A DOSE OF CUP FEVER SO SEVERE, THAT NOT EVEN THE TALENTED DR MILLS-ROBERTS COULD PRESCRIBE A CURE!

YOU SEE, 'TIS THE PASSING—SO ACCURATE!

I'VE NEVER SEEN BETTER!

THERE'LL NOT BE A SINNER ON MARKET COME KICK-OFF!

AYE!

MY MONEY'S ON FRED TO SCORE FIRST!

WHAT MONEY?!

AND, AS THE PLAYERS PUT IN EXTRA PRACTICE...

GOODALL!

SO TOO DID THE FANS!

OI!

PRESTON WAS READY.

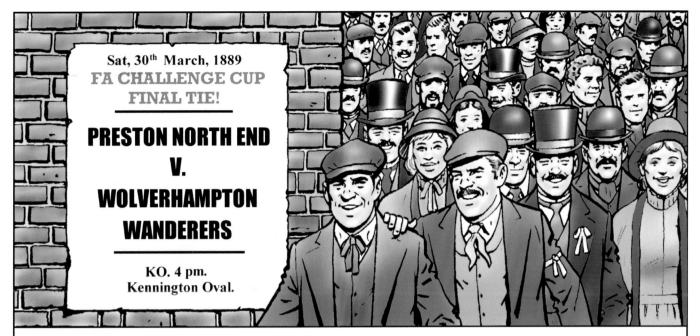

Sat, 30th March, 1889
FA CHALLENGE CUP FINAL TIE!

PRESTON NORTH END
V.
WOLVERHAMPTON WANDERERS

KO. 4 pm.
Kennington Oval.

KICK-OFF WAS ARRANGED FOR 4 O'CLOCK SO AS NOT TO CLASH WITH THE BOAT RACE, AND FROM MIDDAY A TORRENT OF EXCITED FANS SURGED TOWARDS THE PAY GATES OF THE FAMOUS KENNINGTON OVAL. BY 3.40 PM THE GROUND WAS DECLARED FULL, WITH HUNDREDS OF FANS BEING TURNED AWAY.

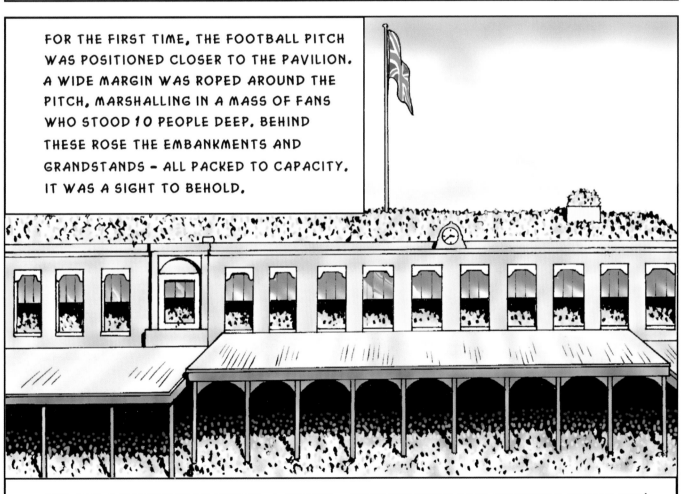

FOR THE FIRST TIME, THE FOOTBALL PITCH WAS POSITIONED CLOSER TO THE PAVILION. A WIDE MARGIN WAS ROPED AROUND THE PITCH, MARSHALLING IN A MASS OF FANS WHO STOOD 10 PEOPLE DEEP. BEHIND THESE ROSE THE EMBANKMENTS AND GRANDSTANDS – ALL PACKED TO CAPACITY. IT WAS A SIGHT TO BEHOLD.

THE OLD PAVILION WAS CHOCK-A-BLOCK – EVEN ITS ROOF WAS CROWNED WITH FANS! IT WAS ESTIMATED OVER 20,000 HAD PAID IN – THE HIGHEST EVER ATTENDANCE FOR A CUP FINAL – AND OF THOSE, ONLY THE MOST ARDENT OF WOLVES SUPPORTERS EXPECTED NORTH END TO LOSE.

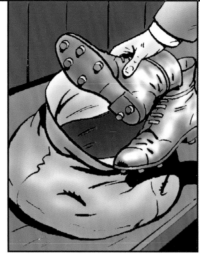

NORTH END LINED-UP:

Dr R. MILLS-ROBERTS

R. HOWARTH

R. HOLMES

G. DRUMMOND

D. RUSSELL

J. GRAHAM

J. GORDON

J. ROSS

J. GOODALL

F. DEWHURST (C.)

S. THOMSON

PREPARE FOR ACTION!

UMPIRE AND ETON LEGEND ARTHUR KINNAIRD GOT PROCEEDINGS UNDERWAY.

A TENSE SUDELL PACED THE TOUCHLINE LIKE A MAN POSSESSED!

WOLVES KICKED-OFF TO A TREMENDOUS ROAR!

PLAY UP, WOLVES!
UP THE WHITES!
HURRAH!

FROM THE OFF, WOLVES WERE DETERMINED TO UNSETTLE NORTH END'S PASSING GAME.

A-AACH!

UGH!

NORTH END RODE THEIR LUCK EARLY ON...

BUT KEPT THEIR COMPOSURE, AND ON *12* MINUTES HOWARTH SET GORDON FREE...

WHO CUT IT BACK FOR JIMMY ROSS...

FRED DEWHURST DIDN'T NEED AN INVITATION!

THE OVAL CROWD EXPLODED!

A GOAL TO THE GOOD, PNE KEPT UP THE PRESSURE, AS GORDON TRIED THE SPECTACULAR!

THEN ON 25 MINUTES, ROSS AND GORDON LINKED UP...

AND...

YET WOLVES WERE MADE OF STERN STUFF, AND CAME BACK FIGHTING IN THE SECOND HALF.

BUT THE DOCTOR'S GOAL STAYED IN TACT!

UNABLE TO GET PAST DR MILLS-ROBERTS AND THE COMMANDING HOLMES AND HOWARTH, WOLVES BEGAN TO TIRE AND NORTH END TOOK CONTROL.

BRAVO!

WOLVES CAN'T GET NEAR 'EM!

THEN, WITH 23 MINUTES LEFT...

HUP!

SAMMY!

3-0!

SAM THOMSON PUT THE GAME BEYOND REACH!

THERE WAS TO BE NO MORE DRAMA, AND WHEN MAJOR MARINDIN BLEW HIS WHISTLE...

PHHEEEEP!

PRESTON NORTH END HAD WON THE FA CUP!

IT'S OVER!

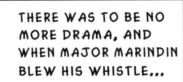

THE OVAL ERUPTED AND THE CELEBRATIONS BEGAN!

HURRAY! HURRAY!

HURRAH!

SUDELL'S MEN HAD FINALLY CLAIMED THE FA CUP - AND THEY'D DONE SO IN SOME STYLE, BY NOT CONCEDING A SINGLE GOAL THOUGHOUT THE TOURNAMENT!

PRESENTATION OF THE TROPHY AND MEDALS WAS TO TAKE PLACE AT THE PRESS SECTION, BUT WITH SO MANY FANS ON THE PITCH IT WAS MOVED TO THE FRONT OF THE PAVILION AND DELAYED UNTIL THE TEAMS HAD CHANGED.

NORTH END'S PLAYERS WANTED WILLIAM SUDELL TO COLLECT THE 'POT', BUT HE INSISTED THE HONOUR STAY WITH THE CAPTAIN. AND SO, AS THE LIGHT BEGAN TO FADE OVER SURREY, FRED DEWHURST STEPPED UP TO RECEIVE THE FAMOUS TROPHY FROM THE FA PRESIDENT MAJOR MARINDIN.

WELL PLAYED, NORTH END!

HURRAY!

HURRAH!

CLAP!

CLAP!

CLAP!

FOR THE PAST FIVE OR SIX YEARS WE HAVE BEEN TRYING HARD TO ACHIEVE THAT WHICH WE HAVE SUCCEEDED IN ACCOMPLISHING TODAY!...

YOU KNOW THE OLD PROVERB SAYS, 'HOPE DEFERRED MAKETH THE HEART SICK, BUT THE LONGER THE DAY IS PUT OFF, THE HAPPIER WE FEEL WHEN IT ARRIVES,'...

ONE OF THE GREATEST PLEASURES IN RECEIVING THIS CUP TODAY, IS TO HAND IT OVER TO THE CUSTODY OF OUR WORTHY FRIEND, MR SUDELL...

MR SUDELL HAS BEEN A FATHER TO THE TEAM – AND IF IT HAD NOT BEEN FOR HIS EXERTIONS, I DO NOT SUPPOSE WE SHOULD'VE BEEN ABLE TO WIN THE CUP!

I CALL ON THE TEAM TO GIVE *THREE HEARTY CHEERS FOR MR SUDELL!*

THIS MOMENT WAS THE CULMINATION OF MANY YEARS' HARD WORK BY MANY HANDS, AND IT WAS ONLY RIGHT THE CAPTAIN'S ELOQUENT SPEECH BE DELIVERED TO A CROWD CONTAINING PNE MEMBERS OLD AND NEW, INCLUDING: JOHN WOODS, JOSEPH BROWN, W.E.M. TOMLINSON, M.P., W. POMFRET, W. ORD, COUNCILLOR WOODS, R. FAZACKERLEY, E.D. HINDLE, H. BALDWIN, E. ALSTON, H. JOHNSON, W. McGUINNESS, G. IDDON, ALDERMAN FORSHAW AND ALDERMAN WALMSLEY.

THE NEWSPAPERS WERE QUICK TO ANOINT THE NEW CHAMPIONS.

LIVERPOOL MERCURY
At last, after a sequence of ill-fortune, the most perfect, the most consistent team ever formed...have attained their just reward.

MANCHESTER GUARDIAN
...by universal consent, the best club in the kingdom.

THE LANCASHIRE EVENING POST
Bravo, North End! Surley your honours list this season ought to convince everyone that what has been said of you, that you are the 'best football team in the world', is every word of it true.

ON MONDAY MORNING IT WAS ANNOUNCED THE **INVINCIBLES** WOULD BE ARRIVING BACK IN PRESTON VIA THE 6.50PM TRAIN FROM LONDON.

BY 7PM UP TO 30,000 PEOPLE LINED THE STREETS, AS WORKERS FLOCKED FROM THE MILLS AND FACTORIES TO WELCOME THEIR TEAM HOME!

HURRAH! HURRAY!

FROM THE RAILWAY STATION, TWO BANDS AND THE VOLUNTEER RIFLES ESCORTED THE TEAM TO A SPECIAL CEREMONY AT THE PUBLIC HALL. AT THE SIGHT OF THE CAVALCADE, THE JUBILANT FOLK OF PRESTON DESCENDED INTO A JOYFUL MADNESS! HATS AND STICKS FLEW INTO THE AIR AMIDST WILD CHEERS, AS THE CROWD SWELLED AND STRAINED TO CATCH A GLIMPSE OF ITS HEROES AND THEIR GLITTERING PRIZE. PRESTON HAD NEVER WITNESSED SUCH SCENES! FOR SUDELL AND THE PLAYERS IT MUST HAVE BEEN A BEAUTIFUL CHAOS.

WILLIAM SUDELL WAS THE TOAST OF PRESTON. THE MAN OF DESTINY WHO PERSEVERED AND FINALLY MADE GOOD HIS QUEST.

SINCE JOINING NORTH END'S CRICKETERS AS A 16 YEAR OLD, SUDELL'S EFFECT HAD BEEN IMMEASURABLE. A BUSINESSMAN AND VISIONARY, HE WAS INSTRUMENTAL IN THE MOVE TO DEEPDALE, THE ATHLETICS EVENTS AND DEVELOPMENT OF THE GROUND. WHILE HIS CLOSE BOND WITH HIS PLAYERS AND INNOVATIVE APPROACH TO TACTICS AND PREPARATION SET THE BLUEPRINT FOR THE MODERN FOOTBALL MANAGER.

THOUGH FUTURE YEARS WOULD BRING A DRAMATIC FALL FROM GRACE, SUDELL'S ROLE IN THE PUSH FOR PROFESSIONALISM AND AS A FOUNDING FATHER OF THE FOOTBALL LEAGUE MEANS HIS LEGACY – NOT JUST AT NORTH END BUT IN THE FOOTBALL WORLD AT LARGE – SHOULD NOT BE OVERLOOKED.

AS FOR THE PLAYERS: THEIR PERFORMANCES HAD BROUGHT AN ATTENTION NEVER BEFORE SEEN. THEY'D BEEN BANNED, EXHAUSTED, AND DEALT THEIR SHARE OF DISAPPOINTMENT. YET THROUGH IT ALL THEY DISPLAYED AN INDOMITABLE SPIRIT TO EMERGE TRIUMPHANT AS THE GREATEST TEAM OF THEIR AGE. IN THE NEXT 127 YEARS, ONLY SIX OTHER CLUBS WOULD MATCH THEIR LEAGUE AND FA CUP DOUBLE, BUT NOT ONE WOULD DO SO UNDEFEATED.

SOMETIME AFTER THE FINAL, **PRESTON NORTH END** POSED OUTSIDE THEIR FULWOOD CLUB HEADQUARTERS. THE PHOTOGRAPH, JUST LIKE THEIR RECORD, WOULD STAND THE TEST OF TIME – THE ICONIC IMAGE OF A TEAM WHO TOUCHED ON PERFECTION AND ENTERED INTO LEGEND, THEIR NAME GILT-EDGED IN HISTORY, FOREVER TO BE CALLED... *INVINCIBLE.*

Lancashire Football Association Cup 1880–89

80–81 Rnd 1 (Away) v. Turton, **L** 6–0.

81–82 Rnd 3 (Away) v. Turton, **L** 8–0.

82–83 Rnd 1 (Away) v. Lower Darwen, **L** 3–2.

83–84 Rnd 1 (Home) v. Lower Darwen, **L** 2–0.

84–85 Rnd 2 (Away) v. Southport, **L** 1–0.

85–86 Semi-Final (Away at Blackburn Rovers' Leamington Road ground) PNE scratched.

86–87 Final (Away at Pikes Lane, Bolton) v. Bolton Wanderers, **W** 3–0. **Champions**.

87–88 Final (Leamington Road) v. Accrington (PNE scratched – fear of crowd trouble).

88–89 PNE Suspended.

FA CUP 1883 to 1889

83–84 Rnd 4 (Home) v. Upton Park, 1–1 (PNE subsequently debarred from the competition).

84–85 Withdrew from the competition.

85–86 Rnd 3 (Away) v. Bolton W., **W** 3–2 (PNE subsequently banned for fielding an ineligible player).

86–87 Semi-Final (Bramall Lane, Sheff) v. West Brom, **L** 2–1.

87–88 Final (The Oval, Surrey) v. West Brom, **L** 2–1.

88–89 Final (The Oval, Surrey) v. Wolverhampton Wanderers, **W** 3–0. **Champions**.

Football League Games 1888–89

Sept 8th H. v. Burnley, **W** 5–2.

Sept 15th A v. Wolves, **W** 4–0.

Sept 22nd H v. Bolton W., **W** 3–1.

Sept 29th A v. Derby County, **W** 3–2.

Oct 6th H v. Stoke City, **W** 7–0.

Oct 13th H v. West Brom, **W** 3–0.

Oct 20th A v. Accrington, 0–0.

Oct 27th H. v. Wolves., **W** 5–2.

Nov 3rd A v. Notts County, **W** 7–0.

Nov 10th H. v. Aston Villa, 1–1.

Nov 12th A. v. Stoke City, **W** 3–0.

Nov 17th H v. Accrington, **W** 2–0.

Nov 24th A v. Bolton W., **W** 5–2.

Dec 8th H v. Derby County, **W** 5–0.

Dec 15th A v. Burnley, 2–2.

Dec 22nd H v. Everton, **W** 3–0.

Dec 26th A v. West Brom, **W** 5–0.

Dec 29th H v. Blackburn R., **W** 1–0.

Jan 5th H v. Notts County, **W** 4–1.*

Jan 12th A v. Blackburn R., 2–2.

Jan 19th A v. Everton, **W** 2–0.

Feb 9th A v. Aston Villa, **W** 2–0.

*Declared Champions.

Football League Appearances 1888–89 (22 Games)

F. Dewhurst 16, G. Drummond 12, J. Edwards 4,
A. Goodall 2, J. Goodall 21, J. Gordon 20, J. Graham 22,
W. Graham 5, R. Holmes 22, R. Howarth 18, J. Inglis 1,
Dr Mills-Roberts 2, A. Robertson 21, J. Ross 21,
D. Russell 18, S. Thomson 16, J. Trainer 20, R. Whittle 1.

Football League Goalscorers 1888–89 (74 Goals)

J. Goodall 20, J. Ross 19, F. Dewhurst 12, J. Gordon 10,
S. Thomson 3, J. Edwards 3, A. Robertson 3, A. Goodall 1,
G. Drummond 1, J. Inglis 1, R. Whittle 1.

FA Cup Games 1888–89

Feb 2nd Rnd 1 A v. Bootle, **W** 3–0.

Feb 16th Rnd 2 A v. Grimsby, **W** 2–0.

Mar 2nd Rnd 3 H v. B'Ham St George, **W** 2–0.

Mar 16th Semi-Final (Bramall Lane, Sheff.) v. West Brom, **W** 1–0.

Mar 30th Final (The Oval, Surrey) v. Wolverhampton W., **W** 3–0. **Champions**.

FA Cup Appearances 1888–89 (5 Games)

Dr Mills-Roberts 5, R. Howarth 5, R. Holmes 5, A. Robertson 1,
G. Drummond 4, Russell 5, J. Graham 5, J. Gordon 5,
J. Ross 5, J. Goodall 5, F. Dewhurst 5, S. Thomson 5.

FA Cup Goalscorers 1888–89 (11 Goals)

S. Thomson 3, J. Goodall 2, J. Ross 2, F. Dewhurst 1,
J. Gordon 1, D. Russell 1, R. Holmes 1.

AUTHOR'S NOTE

Researching the early years of Preston North End was never going to be straightforward for a trainee historian. To this end I am indebted to the work of all North End historians and especially David Hunt, whose epic history of the club (listed in sources) provided an early framework that I could build my book around. Still, I did have to get my hands dirty, and reading through newspaper articles and match reports from the late 19th century at the Harris Reference Library was both rewarding and frustrating. Rewarding in the quality of the prose, considering the reporters were scribbling furiously as the action happened, often unsheltered from the wind and rain. They were a hardy bunch! Frustrating in that there were so many interesting games I've had to omit due to space and time.

There were a few obstacles I had to overcome when visualising the panels. The development of the ground took a little bit of detective work, and I traced its transition from newspaper adverts PNE placed at the time, and from the ground plan of Deepdale drawn up in 1890. The grandstand designs are based on photographs of similar structures from that era, and on a sketch dated 1884 which I found on the internet and has since mysteriously disappeared.

All team kits are based on photos – many of which I saw thanks to the National Football Museum's archive – and the ever helpful Historical Kits website.

North End's first kit of orange and black hoops is based on a Lancashire Evening Post photograph of their rugby team taken in 1877; I can only apologise for showing PNE in orange! From other photographs I deduced that the blue and white hooped strip that followed was then passed on to the reserve team for the 1983–84 season, when the first team began to wear their red and white halved jerseys. The red and white striped jerseys were announced in the Preston Herald as being first worn in October 1885.

Hyde FC's kit in PNE's famous 26–0 victory is one that eluded me, and I ended up basing their blue striped kit on the one worn in a commemorative match played on Deepdale's plastic pitch. For this match it is also possible that PNE wore their red and white stripes. However, we know they'd started wearing white jerseys as early as 1886, and did so initially for special occasions (perhaps to copy the famous Corinthians). I decided they were probably donning white for all their FA Cup matches by late 1886, so I placed them in white from their October 1886 FA Cup match against Queen's Park onwards. A newspaper sketch for their cup tie versus Old Carthusians in the same season also places them in white.

Another consideration was the colour of blue of the shorts. A printed, decorative fixture card from the 1885–86 season, produced by the club, features an illustration of two North End players wearing red and white striped jerseys and royal blue shorts. The colour of the shorts and socks I'd always expected were the famous dark blue, so this threw a new light on things. It is possible the artist was colouring with whatever blue was at hand, and in photos of that kit the tone of blue is difficult to tell. So I went with a slightly lighter shade of dark blue for the shorts and socks up to 1887.

Important dialogue and speeches are taken from sources, except those by Sudell before the Burnley match (first Football League game) and the FA Cup final versus Wolves.

On a final note: After winning the first ever Football League, PNE received no trophy and were instead presented with a special flag. The famous 'lady' trophy (an idea suggested by William Sudell) was not introduced until 1891. PNE of course received the old FA Cup trophy when they completed the double in 1889, but to this day I know of no photograph of the team with the trophy itself. Perhaps there is one out there, waiting to be discovered? The search continues...

ACKNOWLEDGEMENTS

One of the simple joys of writing a book is being able to thank those who have helped along the way, and in this case the list is considerable!

First, a massive thank you to the brilliant David Sque, for taking this project on and bringing the past to life – it has been a privilege working with you. Thank you to Arpad Olbey, for your enthusiasm and continued support, and to my editor, 'The Guardian of Grammar' Stan Carey. Thanks to Steve Hargreaves for your work on our website, and to Tim and Ruben at the printers GraphyCEM.

I'm very grateful to Ben Rhodes, Simon Grayson, the PNEFC marketing team, staff, players, and the club for permission to use their badge. Thanks also to Matt and all the staff at the PNE club shop; to Rainbow House; and to Mark Lawrenson for kindly agreeing to write the foreword. Thank you to Gillian Parkinson, Brian Ellis, and the *Lancashire Evening Post*; and to Simon Thomas of Turner and Brown Accountants. Thanks to our sponsors: Simon Rigby and Richard Simkin from The Villa at North End and Preston Guild Hall; Richard Garratt from Garratts Insurance; and Alexandra Cooper and Chris Dewhurst from Dewhurst Homes.

Help has come from Peter Holme and the National Football Museum; Barney Smith and Preston Digital Archive; and Paul Swarbrick and Blog Preston. My thanks to the staff of the Harris Library and Museum; to Preston City Council for permission to use the town's crest; to Paul McKenzie and *Lancashire Life*; and to John Freeman and his wonderful downthetubes.net website.

I have received great support from Michael Simkin and the staff at Finney's Café and Sports Bar; Jill Rogerson, Michelle Hunt and all at Heartbeat; Phil Whitby, Dan Charnley and the staff of Waterstones, Preston; Steve Stretch and all at GAME Deepdale and GAME Preston; Catherine Bretherton and Cranden Press; and Richard Lowthian of the Ham & Jam Coffee Shop.

Thank you to David Hunt, Mark Naylor, Mark Inglis, Pete Paddock, Gary Bond, Richard Sanders, Ian Rigby, Steve Halliwell, David Hindle, Daniel Carey, David Abbott, and Gary Mounsey (for the kind use of your programme). Thanks to Howard Holmes of FURD; Steven Kay (writer of the fantastic Rabbi Howell book *The Evergreen in Red and White*); Shaun Campbell of the Arthur Wharton Foundation; Paul Brown of the brilliant victorianfootball.co.uk website, and John Lerwill, Aston Villa historian.

I'm appreciative to everyone who bought a ticket and helped promote our 'Be in the Book' raffle, and to everyone who purchased one of our early Invincibles art prints. Recognition must also go to all who helped promote the book in its formative days, and to all the PNE blogs, forums and Twitter accounts which have helped so much. Thanks to all of you who've liked and shared our posts on Facebook and Twitter, or helped spread the word-of-mouth, or displayed leaflets in your shop or pub: your support sustained morale, and I'm sorry I cannot name you all here, only for fear of leaving someone out.

To my wonderful colleagues at the MRI and Radiology Dept at Royal Preston Hospital, thanks for your kind words and interest – alas, no names again for fear of missing one of you out! Thanks to Joan and John Kidman for the loan of your England collection. Thanks to my godparents Pam and Jack Ainsworth, and to my friends Beth, Marie, Pat, Leighton, Dan and Elaine. Special mention to Tize, John Byrne, Bernard and Tomás, and to Keys for your enthusiasm and support when this was just a bean – the required perseverance was forged in wind and rain on Parlick Pike.

Thanks to my family: Dad, Bridget, Sharon and Gary, Bernadette and Winston, Michael and James, and the incredible curly-topped Jayden. And finally to Mum – for a hundred million reasons, this book is as much yours as it is mine.

MJB

SOURCES

BOOKS

James Catton. *Wickets and Goals: Stories of Play.* Chapman & Hall. 1926.

David Hunt. *The History of Preston North End Football Club.* PNE Publications. 2000.

Ian Rigby & Mike Payne. *Loud and Proud, Preston North End FC.* Palatine Books. 2005.

Harry Berry & Geoffrey Allman. *One Hundred Years at Deepdale, 1881–1981.* 1982.

Dave Russell. *Preston North End, 100 Years in the Football League.* Lancs Polytechnic.

David Clayton. *The Preston North End Miscellany.* The History Press. 2010.

Brian Heller. *North End Eleven.* Kindle Edition.

Richard Sanders. *Beastly Fury: The Strange Birth of British Football.* Bantam Press. 2009.

Philip Gibbons. *Association Football in Victorian England.* Minerva Press. 2001.

Paul Brown. *Goal-Post: Victorian Football, Volumes 1 & 2.* Goal-Post/Superelastic 2012/13.

Graham Hughes. *A Devilish Pastime: A History of Football in all its forms.* Sportsbooks. 2009.

Simon Inglis. *League Football and the Men Who Made it.* HarperCollins. 1988.

Mark Metcalf. *The Origins of the Football League: The First Season 1888/89.* Amberley. 2014.

Gordon Small. *The Lancashire Cup: A Complete Record 1879–80 to 2006–7.* SoccerData. 2007.

Peter Holme: *Play Up, Higher Walton!* Landy Publishing. 2006.

Phil Vasili. *The First Black Footballer: Arthur Wharton 1865–1930.* Frank Cass. 1999.

Howard Holmes. *Arthur Wharton: Victorian Sporting Superstar.* FURD Pioneers Comic Book #1.

David Hunt. *A History of Preston.* Carnegie Publishing. 2009.

Keith Johnson. *Preston Remembered.* The History Press. 2011.

Preston History Teachers' Group. *Leisure in 19th Century Preston.* Lancs Education Committee. 1983.

David John Hindle. *Music Hall in Preston: A Gin Palace to a King's Palace.* The History Press. 2007.

Alan Crosby. *A History of Preston Guild: England's Greatest Carnival.* Carnegie. 2012.

The Athletic News. *The Football Annual.* 1880, 1881, 1882.

WEBSITES

www.historicalkits.co.uk / www.spartacus.schoolnet.co.uk / www.victorianfootball.co.uk

www.nationalfootballmuseum.com / gottfriedfuchs.blogspot.co.uk / Preston Digital Archive

NEWSPAPERS

The Preston Chronicle / The Preston Guardian / The Preston Herald / The Lancashire Evening Post
The Illustrated London News / Illustrated Sporting and Dramatic News

Crowd scene fans

A. Martin McLoughlin. **B.** Barbara Bourne.

C. Mark and Harry Garth.

D. Jack Ainsworth.

E. Madeleine Ainsworth.

F. David Ainsworth.

G. Daisy Ainsworth. **H.** Daniel Hollinshead.

I. Margaret Rimmer. **J.** Jason Windsor.

K. Jayden Sutcliffe. **L.** James Sutcliffe.

M. Gary Johnson. **N.** John Murray.

THE
BABY BEAT APPEAL

Registered Charity No: 1051194-7
Sharoe Green Maternity Unit,
Royal Preston, Hospital, Fulwood, Preston PR2 9HT

Helping to save the lives of unborn babies

 Providing funding for research into stillbirths and premature labours

 Providing funding for research into maternal and foetal well-being

 Providing funding for equipment designed to monitor the unborn baby and Mother from conception to birth

 Providing funding for equipment which delivers the very best ante-natal care through to a safe delivery

 Providing funding for bereavement support

 Ensures that the babies born within our community have access to the very latest technology

Every penny donated makes a real difference.

Please help us to help them!

APPEAL OFFICE:
01772 524414
www.babybeat.co.uk